GLENCOE MATHEMATICS

Algebra 1

Chapter 14
Resource Masters

Glencoe
McGraw-Hill

New York, New York
Columbus, Ohio
Chicago, Illinois
Peoria, Illinois
Woodland Hills, California

Consumable Workbooks

Many of the worksheets contained in the Chapter Resource Masters booklets are available as consumable workbooks in both English and Spanish.

Study Guide and Intervention Workbook	0-07-827753-1
Study Guide and Intervention Workbook (Spanish)	0-07-827754-X
Skills Practice Workbook	0-07-827747-7
Skills Practice Workbook (Spanish)	0-07-827749-3
Practice Workbook	0-07-827748-5
Practice Workbook (Spanish)	0-07-827750-7

ANSWERS FOR WORKBOOKS The answers for Chapter 14 of these workbooks can be found in the back of this Chapter Resource Masters booklet.

Glencoe/McGraw-Hill

A Division of The McGraw·Hill Companies

Send all inquiries to:
The McGraw-Hill Companies
8787 Orion Place
Columbus, OH 43240-4027

ISBN: 0-07-827738-8

Algebra 1
Chapter 14 Resource Masters

2 3 4 5 6 7 8 9 10 024 11 10 09 08 07 06 05 04 03

Contents

Teacher's Guide to Using the Chapter 14 Resource Masters

The *Fast File* Chapter Resource system allows you to conveniently file the resources you use most often. The *Chapter 14 Resource Masters* includes the core materials needed for Chapter 14. These materials include worksheets, extensions, and assessment options. The answers for these pages appear at the back of this booklet.

All of the materials found in this booklet are included for viewing and printing in the *Algebra 1 TeacherWorks* CD-ROM.

Vocabulary Builder Pages vii–viii include a student study tool that presents up to twenty of the key vocabulary terms from the chapter. Students are to record definitions and/or examples for each term. You may suggest that students highlight or star the terms with which they are not familiar.

WHEN TO USE Give these pages to students before beginning Lesson 14-1. Encourage them to add these pages to their Algebra Study Notebook. Remind them to add definitions and examples as they complete each lesson.

Study Guide and Intervention
Each lesson in *Algebra 1* addresses two objectives. There is one Study Guide and Intervention master for each objective.

WHEN TO USE Use these masters as reteaching activities for students who need additional reinforcement. These pages can also be used in conjunction with the Student Edition as an instructional tool for students who have been absent.

Skills Practice There is one master for each lesson. These provide computational practice at a basic level.

WHEN TO USE These masters can be used with students who have weaker mathematics backgrounds or need additional reinforcement.

Practice There is one master for each lesson. These problems more closely follow the structure of the Practice and Apply section of the Student Edition exercises. These exercises are of average difficulty.

WHEN TO USE These provide additional practice options or may be used as homework for second day teaching of the lesson.

Reading to Learn Mathematics
One master is included for each lesson. The first section of each master asks questions about the opening paragraph of the lesson in the Student Edition. Additional questions ask students to interpret the context of and relationships among terms in the lesson. Finally, students are asked to summarize what they have learned using various representation techniques.

WHEN TO USE This master can be used as a study tool when presenting the lesson or as an informal reading assessment after presenting the lesson. It is also a helpful tool for ELL (English Language Learner) students.

Enrichment There is one extension master for each lesson. These activities may extend the concepts in the lesson, offer an historical or multicultural look at the concepts, or widen students' perspectives on the mathematics they are learning. These are not written exclusively for honors students, but are accessible for use with all levels of students.

WHEN TO USE These may be used as extra credit, short-term projects, or as activities for days when class periods are shortened.

Assessment Options

The assessment masters in the *Chapter 14 Resources Masters* offer a wide range of assessment tools for intermediate and final assessment. The following lists describe each assessment master and its intended use.

Chapter Assessment

CHAPTER TESTS

- *Form 1* contains multiple-choice questions and is intended for use with basic level students.

- *Forms 2A and 2B* contain multiple-choice questions aimed at the average level student. These tests are similar in format to offer comparable testing situations.

- *Forms 2C and 2D* are composed of free-response questions aimed at the average level student. These tests are similar in format to offer comparable testing situations. Grids with axes are provided for questions assessing graphing skills.

- *Form 3* is an advanced level test with free-response questions. Grids without axes are provided for questions assessing graphing skills.

  All of the above tests include a free-response Bonus question.

- The **Open-Ended Assessment** includes performance assessment tasks that are suitable for all students. A scoring rubric is included for evaluation guidelines. Sample answers are provided for assessment.

- A **Vocabulary Test**, suitable for all students, includes a list of the vocabulary words in the chapter and ten questions assessing students' knowledge of those terms. This can also be used in conjunction with one of the chapter tests or as a review worksheet.

Intermediate Assessment

- Four free-response **quizzes** are included to offer assessment at appropriate intervals in the chapter.

- A **Mid-Chapter Test** provides an option to assess the first half of the chapter. It is composed of both multiple-choice and free-response questions.

Continuing Assessment

- The **Cumulative Review** provides students an opportunity to reinforce and retain skills as they proceed through their study of Algebra 1. It can also be used as a test. This master includes free-response questions.

- The **Standardized Test Practice** offers continuing review of algebra concepts in various formats, which may appear on the standardized tests that they may encounter. This practice includes multiple-choice, grid-in, and quantitative-comparison questions. Bubble-in and grid-in answer sections are provided on the master.

Answers

- Page A1 is an answer sheet for the Standardized Test Practice questions that appear in the Student Edition on pages 794–795. This improves students' familiarity with the answer formats they may encounter in test taking.

- The answers for the lesson-by-lesson masters are provided as reduced pages with answers appearing in red.

- Full-size answer keys are provided for the assessment masters in this booklet.

14 Reading to Learn Mathematics
Vocabulary Builder

This is an alphabetical list of the key vocabulary terms you will learn in Chapter 14. As you study the chapter, complete each term's definition or description. Remember to add the page number where you found the term. Add these pages to your Algebra Study Notebook to review vocabulary at the end of the chapter.

Vocabulary Term	Found on Page	Definition/Description/Example
combination		
complements		
compound event		
dependent events		
empirical study ihm·PIHR·ih·kuhl		
event		
experimental probability		
factorial fak·TOHR·ee·uhl		
Fundamental Counting Principle		

(continued on the next page)

14 **Reading to Learn Mathematics**

Vocabulary Builder (continued)

Vocabulary Term	Found on Page	Definition/Description/Example
inclusive		
independent events		
mutually exclusive		
permutation PUHR·myu·TAY·shuhn		
probability distribution		
probability histogram		
relative frequency		
sample space		
simulation SIHM·yuh·LAY·shuhn		
theoretical probability		
tree diagram		

14-1 Study Guide and Intervention

Counting Outcomes

Lesson 14-1

Tree Diagrams One method used for counting the number of possible outcomes of an event is to draw a **tree diagram**. The last column of the tree diagram shows all of the possible outcomes. The list of all possible outcomes is called the **sample space**, and a specific outcome is called an **event**.

Example 1 Suppose you can set up a stereo system with a choice of video, DVD, or laser disk players, a choice of cassette or graphic equalizer audio components, and a choice of single or dual speakers. Draw a tree diagram to show the sample space.

Player	Audio	Speaker	Outcomes
video	cassette	Single	VCS
		Dual	VCD
	graphic equalizer	Single	VGS
		Dual	VGD
DVD	cassette	Single	DCS
		Dual	DCD
	graphic equalizer	Single	DGS
		Dual	DGD
laser disk	cassette	Single	LCS
		Dual	LCD
	graphic equalizer	Single	LGS
		Dual	LGD

The tree diagram shows that there are 12 ways to set up the stereo system.

Example 2 A food stand offers ice cream cones in vanilla or chocolate flavors. It also offers fudge or caramel toppings, and it uses sugar or cake cones. Use a tree diagram to determine the number of possible ice cream cones.

Flavor	Toppings	Cone	Outcomes
vanilla	fudge	sugar	VFS
		cake	VFC
	caramel	sugar	VCS
		cake	VCC
chocolate	fudge	sugar	CFS
		cake	CFC
	caramel	sugar	CCS
		cake	CCC

The tree diagram shows that there are 8 possible ice cream cones.

Exercises

The spinner at the right is spun twice.

1. Draw a tree diagram to show the sample space.

2. How many outcomes are possible?

A pizza can be ordered with a choice of sausage, pepperoni, or mushrooms for toppings, a choice of thin or pan for the crust, and a choice of medium or large for the size.

3. Draw a tree diagram to show the sample space.

4. How many pizzas are possible?

14-1 Study Guide and Intervention *(continued)*

Counting Outcomes

The Fundamental Counting Principle Another way to count the number of possible outcomes is to use the Fundamental Counting Principle.

Fundamental Counting Principle	If an event *M* can occur in *m* ways and an event *N* can occur in *n* ways, then *M* followed by *N* can occur in *m · n* ways.

Example **Carly and Jake went to an arcade with 9 different games.**

a. In how many different orders can they play the games if they play each one only once?

The number of orders for playing can be found by multiplying the number of choices for each position. Let *n* represent the number of possible orders.

$n = 9 \cdot 8 \cdot 7 \cdot 6 \cdot 5 \cdot 4 \cdot 3 \cdot 2 \cdot 1 = 362,880$

There are 362,880 ways to play each of 9 arcade games once. This is also known as a **factorial**, or $n = 9! = 9 \cdot 8 \cdot 7 \cdot 6 \cdot 5 \cdot 4 \cdot 3 \cdot 2 \cdot 1$.

b. If they have only enough tokens to play 6 different games, how many ways can they do this?

Use the Fundamental Counting Principle to find the sample space. There are 9 choices for the first game, 8 choices for the second, and so on, down to 4 choices for the sixth game.

$n = 9 \cdot 8 \cdot 7 \cdot 6 \cdot 5 \cdot 4 = 60,480$

There are 60,480 ways to play 6 different arcade games once.

Exercises

Find the value of each expression.

1. 6!   **2.** 11!   **3.** 8!

4. A sub sandwich restaurant offers four types of sub sandwiches, three different types of potato chips, five types of bread, and six different beverages. How many different sandwich and drink combinations can you order?

5. How many outfits are possible if you can choose one from each of four shirts, three pairs of pants, two pairs of shoes, and two jackets?

6. In how many ways can you arrange 5 boxes of cereal on a shelf?

7. Seven students sit in a row in the auditorium. In how many ways can they arrange themselves?

8. Kinjal puts 12 different books on a shelf. In how many different ways can she arrange them?

14-1 Skills Practice

Counting Outcomes

Draw a tree diagram to show the sample space for each event. Determine the number of possible outcomes.

1. planting a garden with roses, zinnias, or cosmos, in yellow, red, orange, or purple

2. selecting monogrammed or plain stationery, in white or buff, with lined or unlined envelopes

Find the value of each expression.

3. 1! 1

4. 3!

5. 6!

6. 9!

7. Two dice are rolled. How many outcomes are possible?

8. If students can choose between 7 elective subjects, 6 class periods, and 5 teachers, how many elective classes are possible?

9. How many different ways can a carpenter build a bookcase using one each of 4 types of wood, 3 stains, 5 widths, and 6 heights?

14-1 Practice

Counting Outcomes

Draw a tree diagram to show the sample space for each event. Determine the number of possible outcomes.

1. dining at an Italian, Mexican, or French restaurant, for lunch, early bird (early dinner special), or dinner, and with or without dessert

Find the value of each expression.

2. 5!

3. 8!

4. 10!

5. 12!

6. How many different vacation plans are possible when choosing one each of 12 destinations, 3 lengths of stay, 5 travel options, and 4 types of accommodations?

7. How many different ways can you arrange your work if you can choose from 7 weekly schedules, 6 daily schedules, and one of 3 types of duties?

8. How many different ways can you treat a minor cut if you can choose from 3 methods of cleansing the cut, 5 antibiotic creams, 2 antibacterial sprays, and 6 types of bandages?

9. **TESTING** A teacher gives a quick quiz that has 4 true/false questions and 2 multiple choice questions, each of which has 5 answer choices. In how many ways can the quiz be answered if one answer is given for each question?

CLASS RINGS Students at Pacific High can choose class rings in one each of 8 styles, 5 metals, 2 finishes, 14 stones, 7 cuts of stone, 4 tops, 3 printing styles, and 30 inscriptions.

10. How many different choices are there for a class ring?

11. If a student narrows the choice to 2 styles, 3 metals, 4 cuts of stone, and 5 inscriptions (and has already made the remaining decisions), how many different choices for a ring remain?

14-1 Reading to Learn Mathematics
Counting Outcomes

Pre-Activity **How are possible win/loss football records counted?**

Read the introduction to Lesson 14-1 at the top of page 754 in your textbook. Then complete the diagram.

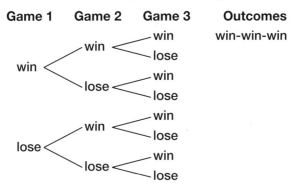

Game 1	Game 2	Game 3	Outcomes
win	win	win	win-win-win
		lose	
	lose	win	
		lose	
lose	win	win	
		lose	
	lose	win	
		lose	

Reading the Lesson

Use the tree diagram above for Exercises 1–4.

1. What is the sample space?

2. Name two different outcomes.

3. Three different outcomes result in a win/loss record of 2-1. What are they?

4. Use the Fundamental Counting Principle to complete the chart.

	Game 1		Game 2		Game 3		Number of Outcomes
Number of Choices		·		·		=	

Helping You Remember

5. Suppose you are training the new disc jockey for a school radio station. He has chosen 10 selections to play from a new CD. How could you use factorials to explain to him the number of different ways the selections could be played?

14-1 Enrichment

Pascal's Triangle

Pascal's Triangle is a pattern of numbers used at many levels of mathematics. It is named for Blaise Pascal, a seventeenth-century French mathematician who discovered several applications of the pattern. However, records of the triangle have been traced as far back as twelfth-century China and Persia. In the year 1303, the Chinese mathematician Zhū-Shìjié wrote *The Precious Mirror of the Four Elements,* in which he described how the triangle could be used to solve polynomial equations. The figure at the right is adapted from the original Chinese manuscript. In the figure, some circles are empty while others contain Chinese symbols.

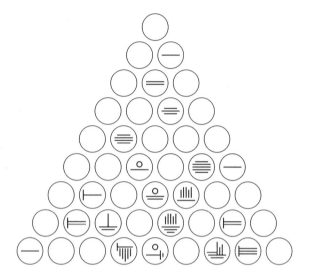

At the right, a portion of Pascal's Triangle is shown using Hindu-Arabic numerals.

The triangle expresses a relationship between numbers that you can discover by comparing the Chinese version and the Hindu-Arabic version.

1. What Chinese symbol corresponds to the Hindu-Arabic numeral 1?

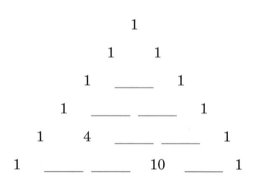

2. Fill in the outermost circles in the Chinese version of Pascal's Triangle.

3. What Chinese symbol corresponds to the Hindu-Arabic numeral 4?

4. What Chinese symbol corresponds to the Hindu-Arabic numeral 10?

5. Based upon your investigation so far, fill in as many of the missing numbers as you can in both the Chinese and Hindu-Arabic versions of Pascal's Triangle.

6. Pascal's Triangle is *symmetric* about an imaginary vertical line that separates the left and right halves of the triangle. Use this fact to fill in more missing numbers in the triangles.

7. Each row of the triangle is generated from the row above by using a simple rule. Find the rule. Then fill in the remaining entries in both triangles.

14-2 Study Guide and Intervention

Permutations and Combinations

Permutations An arrangement or listing in which order or placement is important is called a **permutation**. For example the arrangement AB of choices A and B is different from the arrangement BA of these same two choices.

Permutations	$_nP_r = \dfrac{n!}{(n-r)!}$

Example 1 Find $_6P_2$.

$_nP_r = \dfrac{n!}{(n-r)!}$ Definition of $_nP_r$

$_6P_2 = \dfrac{6!}{(6-2)!}$ $n = 6, r = 2$

$= \dfrac{6!}{4!}$ Simplify.

$= \dfrac{6 \cdot 5 \cdot 4 \cdot 3 \cdot 2 \cdot 1}{4 \cdot 3 \cdot 2 \cdot 1}$ Definition of factorial

$= 6 \cdot 5$ or 30 Simplify.

There are 30 permutations of 6 objects taken 2 at a time.

Example 2 A specific program requires the user to enter a 5-digit password. The digits cannot repeat and can be any five of the digits 1, 2, 3, 4, 7, 8, and 9.

a. How many different passwords are possible?

$_nP_r = \dfrac{n!}{(n-r)!}$

$_7P_5 = \dfrac{7!}{(7-5)!}$

$= \dfrac{7 \cdot 6 \cdot 5 \cdot 4 \cdot 3 \cdot 2 \cdot 1}{2 \cdot 1}$

$= 7 \cdot 6 \cdot 5 \cdot 4 \cdot 3$ or 2520

There are 2520 ways to create a password.

b. What is the probability that the first two digits are odd numbers with the other digits any of the remaining numbers?

$P(\text{first two digits odd}) = \dfrac{\text{number of favorable outcomes}}{\text{number of possible outcomes}}$

Since there are 4 odd digits, the number of choices for the first digit is 4, and the number of choices for the second digit is 3. Then there are 5 choices left for the third digit, 4 for the fourth, and 3 for the fifth, so the number of favorable outcomes is $4 \cdot 3 \cdot 5 \cdot 4 \cdot 3$, or 720.

The probability is $\dfrac{720}{2520} \approx 28.6\%$.

Exercises

Evaluate of each expression.

1. $_7P_4$

2. $_{12}P_7$

3. $(_9P_9)(_{16}P_2)$

4. A club with ten members wants to choose a president, vice-president, secretary, and treasurer. Six of the members are women, and four are men.

     a. How many different sets of officers are possible?

     b. What is the probability that all officers will be women.

     837   *Glencoe Algebra 1*

Lesson 14-2

14-2 Study Guide and Intervention *(continued)*

Permutations and Combinations

Combinations An arrangement or listing in which order is not important is called a **combination**. For example, AB and BA are the same combination of A and B.

Combinations	$_nC_r = \dfrac{n!}{(n-r)!r!}$

Example A club with ten members wants to choose a committee of four members. Six of the members are women, and four are men.

a. How many different committees are possible?

$$_nC_r = \frac{n!}{(n-r)!r!} \qquad \text{Definition of combination}$$

$$= \frac{10!}{(10-4)!4!} \qquad n = 10, r = 4$$

$$= \frac{10 \cdot 9 \cdot 8 \cdot 7}{4!} \qquad \text{Divide by the GCF 6!.}$$

$$= 210 \qquad \text{Simplify.}$$

There are 210 ways to choose a committee of four when order is not important.

b. If the committee is chosen randomly, what is the probability that two members of the committee are men?

There are $_4C_2 = \dfrac{4!}{(4-2)!2!} = 6$ ways to choose two men randomly, and there are

$_6C_2 = \dfrac{6!}{(6-4)!4!} = 15$ ways to choose two women randomly. By the Fundamental

Counting Principle, there are $6 \cdot 15$ or 90 ways to choose a committee with two men and two women.

$$\text{Probability (2 men and 2 women)} = \frac{\text{number of favorable outcomes}}{\text{number of possible outcomes}}$$

$$= \frac{90}{210} \text{ or about } 42.9\%$$

Exercises

Find the value of each expression.

1. $_7C_3$

2. $_{12}C_8$

3. $(_9C_9)(_{11}C_9)$

4. In how many ways can a club with 9 members choose a two-member sub-committee?

5. A book club offers its members a book each month for a year from a selection of 24 books. Ten of the books are biographies and 14 of the books are fiction.

    a. How many ways could the members select 12 books?

    b. What is the probability that 5 biographies and 7 fiction books will be chosen?

14-2 **Skills Practice**

Permutations and Combinations

Determine whether each situation involves a *permutation* or *combination*. Explain your reasoning.

1. dinner guests seated around a table

2. a pattern of different widths of bars and spaces for a bar code

3. selecting two yellow marbles out of a sack of yellow and blue marbles

4. placing one can of each of 15 different types of soup along a store shelf

5. selecting four candles from a box of ten

6. the placement of the top ten finishers in a school's spelling bee

7. choosing two colors of paint out of twenty to paint the walls and trim of a bedroom

8. choosing a set of twelve pencils from a selection of thirty-six

Evaluate each expression.

9. $_5P_2$

10. $_6P_4$

11. $_7P_3$

12. $_9P_4$

13. $_7P_5$

14. $_5P_3$

15. $_6C_2$

16. $_9C_7$

17. $_8C_4$

18. $_7C_5$

19. $_{12}C_2$

20. $_{13}C_7$

21. $_{11}C_2$

22. $_5P_4$

23. $_{14}C_5$

24. $_{11}C_6$

25. $(_4P_2)(_3P_2)$

26. $(_8C_6)(_5P_1)$

Lesson 14-2

14-2 Practice

Permutations and Combinations

Determine whether each situation involves a *permutation* or *combination*. Explain your reasoning.

1. choosing two dogs from a litter of two males and three females

2. a simple melody formed by playing the notes on 8 different piano keys

3. a selection of nine muffins from a shelf of twenty-three

4. the selection of a four-letter acronym (word formed from the initial letters of other words) in which two of the letters cannot be C or P

5. choosing an alphanumeric password to access a website

Evaluate each expression.

6. $_{11}P_3$

7. $_6P_3$

8. $_{15}P_3$

9. $_{10}C_9$

10. $_{12}C_9$

11. $_7C_3$

12. $_7C_4$

13. $_{12}C_4$

14. $_{13}P_3$

15. $\left(_8C_4\right)\left(_8C_5\right)$

16. $\left(_{17}C_2\right)\left(_8C_6\right)$

17. $\left(_{16}C_{15}\right)\left(_{16}C_1\right)$

18. $\left(_8P_3\right)\left(_8P_2\right)$

19. $\left(_5P_4\right)\left(_6P_5\right)$

20. $\left(_{13}P_1\right)\left(_{15}P_1\right)$

21. $\left(_{10}C_3\right)\left(_{10}P_3\right)$

22. $\left(_{15}P_4\right)\left(_4C_3\right)$

23. $\left(_{14}C_7\right)\left(_{15}P_3\right)$

24. **SPORT** In how many orders can the top five finishers in a race finish?

JUDICIAL PROCEDURE The court system in a community needs to assign 3 out of 8 judges to a docket of criminal cases. Five of the judges are male and three are female.

25. Does the selection of judges involve a permutation or a combination?

26. In how many ways could three judges be chosen?

27. If the judges are chosen randomly, what is the probability that all 3 judges are male?

14-2 Reading to Learn Mathematics

Permutations and Combinations

Pre-Activity   **How can combinations be used to form committees?**

Read the introduction to Lesson 14-2 at the top of page 760 in your textbook.

What is meant by the term *combination*?

Reading the Lesson

Complete the chart.

	Situation	Permutation or Combination?	Explain Your Choice
1.	3 of 7 students are chosen to go to a job fair		
2.	arrangement of student work for the school art show		
3.	4-digit student I.D. numbers		
4.	choosing 4 out of 12 possible pizza toppings		

Helping You Remember

5. To help you remember how the terms *permutation* and *combination* are different, think of everyday words that start with the letters P and C and that illustrate the meaning of each word. Explain how the words illustrate the two terms.

Lesson 14-2

14-2 **Enrichment**

Latin Squares

In designing a statistical experiment, it is important to try to randomize the variables. For example, suppose 4 different motor oils are being compared to see which give the best gasoline mileage. An experimenter might then choose 4 different drivers and four different cars. To test-drive all the possible combinations, the experimenter would need 64 test-drives.

To reduce the number of test drives, a statistician might use an arrangement called a **Latin Square**.

For this example, the four motor oils are labeled A, B, C, and D and are arranged as shown. Each oil must appear exactly one time in each row and column of the square.

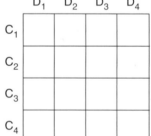

The drivers are labeled D_1, D_2, D_3, and D_4; the cars are labeled C_1, C_2, C_3, and C_4.

Now, the number of test-drives is just 16, one for each cell of the Latin Square.

Create two 4-by-4 Latin Squares that are different from the example.

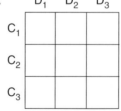

Make three different 3-by-3 Latin Squares.

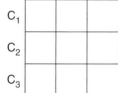

14-3 Study Guide and Intervention

Probability of Compound Events

Independent and Dependent Events Compound events are made up of two or more simple events. The events can be **independent events** or they can be **dependent events**.

Probability of Independent Events	Outcome of first event does not affect outcome of second.	$P(A \text{ and } B) =$ $P(A) \cdot P(B)$	Example: rolling a 6 on a die and then rolling a 5
Probability of Dependent Events	Outcome of first event does affect outcome of second.	$P(A \text{ and } B) =$ $P(A) \cdot P(B \text{ following } A)$	Example: without replacing the first card, choosing an ace and then a king from a deck of cards

Example 1 Find the probability that you will roll a six and then a five when you roll a die twice.

By the definition of independent events, $P(A \text{ and } B) = P(A) \cdot P(B)$

First roll: $P(6) = \dfrac{1}{6}$

Second roll: $P(5) = \dfrac{1}{6}$

$P(6 \text{ and } 5) = P(6) \cdot P(5)$

$\qquad = \dfrac{1}{6} \cdot \dfrac{1}{6}$

$\qquad = \dfrac{1}{36}$

The probability that you will roll a six and then roll a five is $\dfrac{1}{36}$.

Example 2 A bag contains 3 red marbles, 2 green marbles, and 4 blue marbles. Two marbles are drawn randomly from the bag and not replaced. Find the probability that both marbles are blue.

By the definition of dependent events, $P(A \text{ and } B) = P(A) \cdot P(B \text{ following } A)$

First marble: $P(\text{blue}) = \dfrac{4}{9}$

Second marble: $P(\text{blue}) = \dfrac{3}{8}$

$P(\text{blue, blue}) = \dfrac{4}{9} \cdot \dfrac{3}{8}$

$\qquad = \dfrac{12}{72}$

$\qquad = \dfrac{1}{6}$

The probability of drawing two blue marbles is $\dfrac{1}{6}$.

Exercises

A bag contains 3 red, 4 blue, and 6 yellow marbles. One marble is selected at a time, and once a marble is selected, it is not replaced. Find each probability.

1. $P(2 \text{ yellow})$ **2.** $P(\text{red, yellow})$ **3.** $P(\text{blue, red, yellow})$

4. George has two red socks and two white socks in a drawer. What is the probability of picking a red sock and a white sock in that order if the first sock is not replaced?

5. Phyllis drops a penny in a pond, and then she drops a nickel in the pond. What is the probability that both coins land with tails showing?

6. A die is rolled and a penny is dropped. Find the probability of rolling a two and showing a tail.

Lesson 14-3

14-3 **Study Guide and Intervention** (continued)

Probability of Compound Events

Mutually Exclusive and Inclusive Events Events that cannot occur at the same time are called **mutually exclusive**. If two events are not mutually exclusive, they are called **inclusive**.

Probability of Mutually Exclusive Events	$P(A \text{ or } B) = P(A) + P(B)$	$P(\text{rolling a 2 or a 3 on a die}) = P(2) + P(3) = \frac{1}{3}$
Probability of Inclusive Events	$P(A \text{ or } B) =$ $P(A) + P(B) - P(A \text{ and } B)$	$P(\text{King or Heart}) = P(K) + P(H) - P(K \text{ and } H) = \frac{9}{26}$

Example Suppose a card is drawn from a standard deck of 52 cards. Find the probability of drawing a king or a queen.

Drawing a king or a queen are mutually exclusive events.
By the definition of mutually exclusive events, $P(A \text{ or } B) = P(A) + P(B)$.

$P(A) = P(\text{king}) = \frac{4}{52} = \frac{1}{13}$ $P(B) = P(\text{queen}) = \frac{4}{52} = \frac{1}{13}$

$P(\text{king or queen}) = \frac{1}{13} + \frac{1}{13}$

$= \frac{2}{13}$

The probability of drawing a king or a queen is $\frac{2}{13}$.

Exercises

A bag contains 2 red, 5 blue, and 7 yellow marbles. Find each probability.

1. $P(\text{yellow or red})$ **2.** $P(\text{red or not yellow})$ **3.** $P(\text{blue or red or yellow})$

One card is drawn from a standard deck of 52 cards. Find each probability.

4. $P(\text{jack or red})$

5. $P(\text{red or black})$

6. $P(\text{jack or clubs})$

7. $P(\text{queen or less than 3})$

8. $P(5 \text{ or } 6)$

9. $P(\text{diamond or spade})$

10. In a math class, 12 out of 15 girls are 14 years old and 14 out of 17 boys are 14 years old. What is the probability of selecting a girl or a 14-year old from this class?

14-3 Skills Practice

Probability of Compound Events

A bag contains 2 green, 9 brown, 7 yellow, and 4 blue marbles. Once a marble is selected, it is not replaced. Find each probability.

1. P(brown, then yellow)

2. P(green, then blue)

3. P(yellow, then yellow)

4. P(blue, then blue)

5. P(green, then *not* blue)

6. P(brown, then *not* green)

A die is rolled and a spinner like the one at the right is spun. Find each probability.

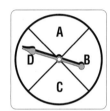

7. P(4 and A)

8. P(an even number and C)

9. P(2 or 5 and B or D)

10. P(a number less than 5 and B, C, or D)

One card is drawn from a standard deck of 52 cards. Find each probability.

11. P(jack or ten)

12. P(red or black)

13. P(queen or club)

14. P(red or ace)

15. P(diamond or black)

16. P(face card or spade)

Tiles numbered 1 through 20 are placed in a box. Tiles numbered 11 through 30 are placed in a second box. The first tile is randomly drawn from the first box. The second tile is randomly drawn from the second box. Find each probability.

17. P(both are greater than 15)

18. The first tile is odd and the second tile is less than 25.

19. The first tile is a multiple of 6 and the second tile is a multiple of 4.

20. The first tile is less than 15 and the second tile is even or greater than 25.

14-3 Practice

Probability of Compound Events

A bag contains 5 red, 3 brown, 6 yellow, and 2 blue marbles. Once a marble is selected, it is not replaced. Find each probability.

1. P(brown, then yellow, then red)

2. P(red, then red, then blue)

3. P(yellow, then yellow, then *not* blue)

4. P(brown, then brown, then *not* yellow)

A die is rolled and a card is drawn from a standard deck of 52 cards. Find each probability.

5. P(6 and king)

6. P(odd number and black)

7. P(less than 3 and heart)

8. P(greater than 1 and black ace)

One card is drawn from a standard deck of 52 cards. Find each probability.

9. P(spade or numbered card)

10. P(ace or red queen)

11. P(red or *not* face card)

12. P(heart or *not* queen)

Tiles numbered 1 through 25 are placed in a box. Tiles numbered 11 through 30 are placed in a second box. The first tile is randomly drawn from the first box. The second tile is randomly drawn from the second box. Find each probability.

13. P(both are greater than 15 and less than 20)

14. The first tile is greater than 10 and the second tile is less than 25 or even.

15. The first tile is a multiple of 3 or prime and the second tile is a multiple of 5.

16. The first tile is less than 9 or odd and the second tile is a multiple of 4 or less than 21.

17. WEATHER The forecast predicts a 40% chance of rain on Tuesday and a 60% chance on Wednesday. If these probabilities are independent, what is the chance that it will rain on both days?

FOOD Tomaso places favorite recipes in a bag for 4 pasta dishes, 5 casseroles, 3 types of chili, and 8 desserts.

18. If Tomaso chooses one recipe at random, what is the probability that he selects a pasta dish or a casserole?

19. If Tomaso chooses one recipe at random, what is the probability that he does *not* select a dessert?

20. If Tomaso chooses two recipes at random without replacement, what is the probability that the first recipe he selects is a casserole and the second recipe he selects is a dessert?

14-3 Reading to Learn Mathematics

Probability of Compound Events

Pre-Activity   **How are probabilities used by meteorologists?**

Read the introduction to Lesson 14-3 at the top of page 769 in your textbook.

Is it more likely to rain or not rain on Saturday? on Sunday? Explain.

Reading the Lesson

1. Complete the chart.

Term	Example	Formula
independent events	Rolling two dice	$P(A \text{ and } B) = P(A) \cdot P(B)$
dependent events		
mutually exclusive events		
inclusive events		

2. In probability, what is meant by the phrase *with replacement*?

Helping You Remember

3. Look up the following terms in a dictionary. Write the definitions that best relate to the way these terms are used in probability.

independent _____

dependent _____

exclusive _____

inclusive _____

Lesson 14-3

14-3 **Enrichment**

Conditional Probability

The probability of an event given the occurrence of another event is called **conditional probability**. The conditional probability of event A given event B is denoted $P(A)B)$.

Example **Suppose a pair of number cubes is rolled. It is known that the sum is greater than seven. Find the probability that the number cubes match.**

There are 15 sums greater than seven and there are 36 possible pairs altogether.

$$P(B) = \frac{15}{36}$$

$$P(A)B) = \frac{P(A \text{ and } B)}{P(B)}$$

$$= \frac{\frac{3}{36}}{\frac{15}{36}} \text{ or } \frac{1}{5}$$

There are three matching pairs greater than seven, $(4, 4)$, $(5, 5)$, and $(6, 6)$.

$$P(A \text{ and } B) = \frac{3}{36}$$

The conditional probability is $\frac{1}{5}$.

A card is drawn from a standard deck of 52 cards and is found to be red. Given that event, find each of the following probabilities.

1. $P(\text{heart})$

2. $P(\text{ace})$

3. $P(\text{face card})$

4. $P(\text{jack or ten})$

5. $P(\text{six of spades})$

6. $P(\text{six of hearts})$

A sports survey taken at Stirers High School shows that 48% of the respondents liked soccer, 66% liked basketball, and 38% liked hockey. Also, 30% liked soccer and basketball, 22% liked basketball and hockey, and 28% liked soccer and hockey. Finally, 12% liked all three sports.

7. Find the probability that Meg likes soccer if she likes basketball.

8. Find the probability that Juan likes basketball if he likes soccer.

9. Find the probability that Mieko likes hockey if she likes basketball.

10. Find the probability that Greg likes hockey if he likes soccer.

14-4 # Study Guide and Intervention

Probability Distributions

Random Variables and Probability Distributions A random variable X is a variable whose value is the numerical outcome of a random event.

Example A teacher asked her students how many siblings they have. The results are shown in the table at the right.

Number of Siblings	Number of Students
0	1
1	15
2	8
3	2
4	1

a. Find the probability that a randomly selected student has 2 siblings.

The random variable X can equal 0, 1, 2, 3, or 4. In the table, the value $X = 2$ is paired with 8 outcomes, and there are 27 students surveyed.

$$P(X = 2) = \frac{2 \text{ siblings}}{27 \text{ students surveyed}}$$

$$= \frac{8}{27}$$

The probability that a randomly selected student has 2 siblings is $\frac{8}{27}$, or 29.6%.

b. Find the probability that a randomly selected student has at least three siblings.

$$P(X \geq 3) = \frac{2 + 1}{27}$$

The probability that a randomly selected student has at least 3 siblings is $\frac{1}{9}$, or 11.1%.

Exercises

For Exercises 1–3, use the grade distribution shown at the right. A grade of A = 5, B = 4, C = 3, D = 2, F = 1.

X = Grade	5	4	3	2	1
Number of Students	6	9	5	4	1

1. Find the probability that a randomly selected student in this class received a grade of C.

2. Find the probability that a randomly selected student in this class received a grade lower than a C.

3. What is the probability that a randomly selected student in this class passes the course, that is, gets at least a D?

4. The table shows the results of tossing 3 coins 50 times. What is the probability of getting 2 or 3 heads?

X = Number of Heads	0	1	2	3
Number of Times	6	20	19	5

Lesson 14-4

14-4 Study Guide and Intervention *(continued)*

Probability Distributions

Probability Distributions The probabilities associated with every possible value of the random variable X make up what are called the **probability distribution** for that variable. A probability distribution has the following properties.

Properties of a Probability Distribution	1. The probability of each value of X is greater than or equal to 0. 2. The probabilities for all values of X add up to 1.

The probability distribution for a random variable can be given in a table or in a **probability histogram** and used to obtain other information.

Example The data from the example on page 849 can be used to determine a probability distribution and to make a probability histogram.

X = Number of Siblings	P(X)
0	0.037
1	0.556
2	0.296
3	0.074
4	0.037

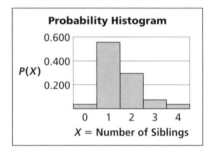

Probability Histogram

$P(X)$ — X = Number of Siblings

a. Show that the probability distribution is valid.

For each value of X, the probability is greater than or equal to 0 and less than or equal to 1. Also, the sum of the probabilities is 1.

b. What is the probability that a student chosen at random has fewer than 2 siblings?

Because the events are independent, the probability of fewer than 2 siblings is the sum of the probability of 0 siblings and the probability of 1 sibling, or $0.037 + 0.556 = 0.593$.

Exercises

The table at the right shows the probability distribution for students by school enrollment in the United States in 1997. Use the table for Exercises 1–3.

X = Type of School	P(X)
Elementary = 1	0.562
Secondary = 2	0.219
Higher Education = 3	0.219

Source: *The New York Times Almanac*

1. Show that the probability distribution is valid.

2. If a student is chosen at random, what is the probability that the student is in elementary or secondary school?

3. Make a probability histogram of the data.

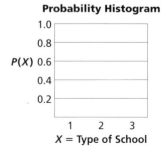

Probability Histogram

$P(X)$ — X = Type of School

14-4 **Skills Practice**

Probability Distributions

For Exercises 1–3, the spinner shown is spun three times.

1. Write the sample space with all possible outcomes.

2. Find the probability distribution X, where X represents the number of times the spinner lands on green for $X = 0$, $X = 1$, $X = 2$, and $X = 3$.

3. Make a probability histogram.

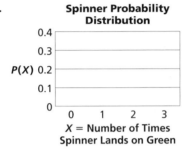

For Exercises 4–7, the spinner shown is spun two times.

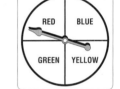

4. Write the sample space with all possible outcomes.

5. Find the probability distribution X, where X represents the number of times the spinner lands on yellow for $X = 0$, $X = 1$, and $X = 2$.

6. Make a probability histogram.

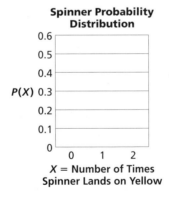

BUSINESS For Exercises 7–9, use the table that shows the probability distribution of the number of minutes a customer spends at the express checkout at a supermarket.

X = Minutes	1	2	3	4	5+
Probability	0.09	0.13	0.28	0.32	0.18

7. Show that this is a valid probability distribution.

8. What is the probability that a customer spends less than 3 minutes at the checkout?

9. What is the probability that the customer spends at least 4 minutes at the checkout?

Lesson 14-4

14-4 Practice

Probability Distributions

For Exercises 1–3, the spinner shown is spun two times.

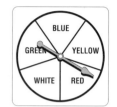

1. Write the sample space with all possible outcomes.

2. Find the probability distribution X, where X represents the number of times the spinner lands on blue for $X = 0$, $X = 1$, and $X = 2$.

3. Make a probability histogram.

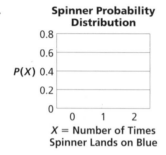

Spinner Probability Distribution

X = Number of Times Spinner Lands on Blue

TELECOMMUNICATIONS For Exercises 4–6, use the table that shows the probability distribution of the number of telephones per student's household at Wilson High.

X = Number of Telephones	1	2	3	4	5+
Probability	0.01	0.16	0.34	0.39	0.10

4. Show that this is a valid probability distribution.

5. If a student is chosen at random, what is the probability that there are more than 3 telephones at the student's home?

6. Make a probability histogram.

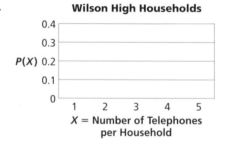

Wilson High Households

X = Number of Telephones per Household

LANDSCAPING For Exercises 7–9, use the table that shows the probability distribution of the number of shrubs (rounded to the nearest 50) ordered by corporate clients of a landscaping company over the past five years.

Number of Shrubs	50	100	150	200	250
Probability	0.11	0.24	0.45	0.16	0.04

7. Define a random variable and list its values.

8. Show that this is a valid probability distribution.

9. What is the probability that a client's (rounded) order was at least 150 shrubs?

14-4 Reading to Learn Mathematics

Probability Distributions

Pre-Activity **How can a pet store owner use a probability distribution?**

Read the introduction to Lesson 14-4 at the top of page 777 in your textbook.

- How many customers did the store owner survey?

- Based on the survey, it is most likely that a customer would have

  _____ pet(s) and least likely that they would have _____ pet(s).

Reading the Lesson

The table below shows the probability of various family sizes in the United States.

Family Size (United States)	
X = Size of Family	Probability
2	0.42
3	0.23
4	0.21
5	0.10
6	0.03
7	0.01

Source: *Statistical Abstract of the United States*

1. For each value of X, is the probability greater than or equal to 0 and less than or equal to 1?

2. What is the sum of the probabilities?

3. Is the probability distribution valid?

4. Complete the probability histogram of the data.

Title: _____

Helping You Remember

5. Use the outcomes of tossing a coin to describe how the probabilities of the possible outcomes add up to 1.

Lesson 14-4

14-4 Enrichment

Golden Rectangles

A **golden rectangle** has the property that its sides satisfy the following proportion.

$$\frac{a + b}{a} = \frac{a}{b}$$

Two quadratic equations can be written from the proportion. These are sometimes called **golden quadratic** equations.

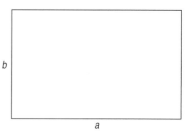

1. In the proportion, let $a = 1$. Use cross-multiplication to write a quadratic equation.

2. Solve the equation in Exercise 1 for b.

3. In the proportion, let $b = 1$. Write a quadratic equation in a.

4. Solve the equation in Exercise 3 for a.

5. Explain why $\frac{1}{2}(\sqrt{5} + 1)$ and $\frac{1}{2}(\sqrt{5} - 1)$ are called golden ratios.

Another property of golden rectangles is that a square drawn inside a golden rectangle creates another, smaller golden rectangle.

In the design at the right, opposite vertices of each square have been connected with quarters of circles.

For example, the arc from point B to point C is created by putting the point of a compass at point A. The radius of the arc is the length BA.

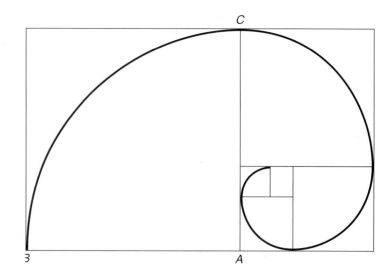

6. On a separate sheet of paper, draw a larger version of the design. Start with a golden rectangle with a long side of 10 inches.

14-5 Study Guide and Intervention

Probability Simulations

Theoretical and Experimental Probability The probability used to describe events mathematically is called **theoretical probability**. For example, the mathematical probability of rolling a 4 with a number cube is $\frac{1}{6}$, or $P(4) = \frac{1}{6}$. **Experimental probability** is the ratio of the number of times an outcome occurs in an experiment to the total number of events or trials, known as the **relative frequency**.

Experimental probability	$\dfrac{\text{frequency of an outcome}}{\text{total number of trials}}$

Example 1 Matt recorded that it rained 8 times in November and snowed 3 times. The other days, it was sunny. There are 30 days in November. Suppose Matt uses these results to predict November's weather next year. What is the probability that a day in November will be sunny?

$$\text{Experimental Probability} = \frac{\text{frequency of outcome}}{\text{total number of trials}}$$

$$= \frac{(30 - 8 - 3)}{30}$$

$$= \frac{19}{30} = 63.3\%$$

The probability that it will be sunny on a day in November is 63.3%.

Example 2 A football team noticed that 9 of the last 20 coin tosses to choose which team would receive the ball first resulted in tails. What is the experimental probability of the coin landing on tails? What is the theoretical probability?

$$\text{Experimental Probability} = \frac{\text{frequency of outcome}}{\text{total number of trials}}$$

$$= \frac{\text{number of tails}}{\text{total number of tosses}}$$

$$= \frac{9}{20} = 45\%$$

In this case, the experimental probability that a coin toss will be tails is 45%. If the coin is fair, the mathematical probability is 50%.

Exercises

A math class decided to test whether a die is fair, that is, whether the experimental probability equals the theoretical probability. The results for 100 rolls are shown at the right. Use the information for Exercises 1–3.

1: 1	2: 15
3: 4	4: 13
5: 15	6: 42

1. What is the theoretical probability of rolling a 6?

2. What is the experimental probability of rolling a 6?

3. Is the die fair? Explain your reasoning.

Lesson 14-5

14-5 Study Guide and Intervention *(continued)*

Probability Simulations

Performing Simulations A method that is often used to find experimental probability is a **simulation**. A simulation allows you to use objects to act out an event that would be difficult or impractical to perform.

Example In one baseball season, Pete was able to get a base hit 42 of the 254 times he was at bat.

a. What could be used to simulate his getting a base hit?

First find the experimental probability.

$$\text{Experimental Probability} = \frac{\text{frequency of outcome}}{\text{total number of trials}}$$

$$= \frac{42}{254} \text{ or } 16.5\%$$

Notice that the experimental probability is about $\frac{1}{6}$. Therefore use a spinner like the one at the right with 6 equally likely outcomes.

b. Describe a way to simulate his next 10 times at bat.

Let an outcome of 1 correspond to Pete's getting a base hit. Let all other outcomes correspond to his *not* getting a hit. Spin the spinner once to simulate a time at bat. Record the result and repeat this 9 more times.

Exercises

1. What could you use to simulate the outcome of guessing on a 20 question true-false test?

2. What could you use to simulate the outcome of guessing on a 20-question multiple choice test with 4 alternative answers labeled A, B, C, and D for each question?

For Exercises 3–4, use the following information.

Main Street Supermarket randomly gives each shopper a free two-liter bottle of cola during the Saturday shopping hours. The supermarket sells 6 different types of cola.

3. What could be used to perform a simulation of this situation?

4. How could you use this simulation to model the next 50 bottles of cola given out.

5. At a picnic, there were 2 peanut butter sandwiches, 2 chicken sandwiches, a tuna sandwich, and a turkey sandwich in a cooler. Describe a simulation that could be used to find the probability of randomly picking a certain sandwich from the cooler.

14-5 # Skills Practice

Probability Simulations

For Exercises 1–3, use a standard deck of 52 cards. Select a card at random, record the suit of the card (heart, diamond, club, or spade), and then replace the card. Repeat this procedure 26 times.

1. Based on your results, what is the experimental probability of selecting a heart?

2. Based on your results, what is the experimental probability of selecting a diamond or a spade?

3. Compare your results to the theoretical probabilities.

4. There are 3 siblings in the Bencievenga family. What could you use to simulate the genders of the 3 siblings?

5. A random survey of 23 students revealed that 2 students walk to school, 12 ride the bus, 6 drive a car, and 3 ride with a parent or other adult. What could you use for a simulation to determine the probability that a student selected at random uses any one type of transportation?

BIOLOGY For Exercises 6–9, use the following information.

Stephen conducted a survey of the students in his classes to observe the distribution of eye color. The table shows the results of his survey.

Eye Color	Blue	Brown	Green	Hazel
Number	12	58	2	8

6. Find the experimental probability distribution for each eye color.

7. Based on the survey, what is the experimental probability that a student in Stephen's classes has blue or green eyes?

8. Based on the survey, what is the experimental probability that a student in Stephen's classes does *not* have green or hazel eyes?

9. If the distribution of eye color in Stephen's grade is similar to the distribution in his classes, about how many of the 360 students in his grade would be expected to have brown eyes?

Lesson 14-5

14-5 Practice

Probability Simulations

For Exercises 1–3, place 5 red, 4 yellow, and 7 green marbles in a box. Randomly draw two marbles from the box, record each color, and then return the marbles to the box. Repeat this procedure 50 times.

1. Based on your results, what is the experimental probability of selecting two yellow marbles?

2. Based on your results, what is the experimental probability of selecting a green marble and a yellow marble?

3. Compare your results to the theoretical probabilities.

4. Color blindness occurs in 4% of the male population. What could you use to simulate this situation?

SCHOOL CURRICULUM For Exercises 5–8, use the following information.

Laurel Woods High randomly selected students for a survey to determine the most important school issues among the student body. The school wants to develop a curriculum that addresses these issues. The survey results are shown in the table.

5. Find the experimental probability distribution of the importance of each issue.

School Issues	
Issue	Number Ranking Issue Most Important
Grades	37
School Standards	17
Popularity	84
Dating	76
Violence	68
Drugs, including tobacco	29

6. Based on the survey, what is the experimental probability that a student chosen at random thinks the most important issue is grades or school standards?

7. The enrollment in the 9th and 10th grades at Laurel Woods High is 168. If their opinions are reflective of those of the school as a whole, how many of them would you expect to have chosen popularity as the most important issue?

8. Suppose the school develops a curriculum incorporating the top three issues. What is the probability that a student selected at random will think the curriculum addresses the most important issue at school?

14-5 Reading to Learn Mathematics

Probability Simulations

Pre-Activity **How can probability simulations be used in health care?**

Read the introduction to Lesson 14-5 at the top of page 782 in your textbook.

- What does success mean in this study?

- Since there were 100 people in each study group, what does each number in the chart represent?

Reading the Lesson

For each situation described below, choose the manipulative you would use to simulate the problem. Explain your choice.

	Situation	Simulation method
1.	58% of drivers (commercial and private vehicles) have a cell phone in their car. Simulate whether or not the next 10 drivers you meet on the road will have a cell phone.	• die • coins • marbles • spinner
2.	A restaurant has six types of coloring books to give away with children's meals. Simulate finding which coloring books are given away with the next 15 children's meals that are ordered.	• die • coins • marbles • spinner

Helping You Remember

3. In your own words, explain the difference between theoretical probability and experimental probability.

14-5 **Enrichment**

The Work Problem and Similar Right Triangles

"The work problem" has been included in algebra textbooks for a very long time. In older books, the people in the problem always seemed to be digging ditches.

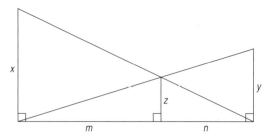

If Olivia can dig a ditch in x hours and George can dig the same ditch in y hours, how long will it take them to dig the ditch if they work together?

You have learned a way to solve this type of problem using rational equations. It can also be solved using a geometric model that uses two overlapping right triangles.

In the drawing, the length x is Olivia's time. The length y is George's time. The answer to the problem is the length of the segment z. The distance $m + n$ can be any convenient length.

Solve each problem.

1. Solve the work problem for $x = 6$ and $y = 3$ by drawing a diagram and measuring.

2. Confirm your solution to Exercise 1 by writing and solving a rational equation.

3. On a separate sheet of paper, create a word problem to go with the values $x = 6$ and $y = 3$.

4. On a separate sheet of paper, solve this problem with a diagram. Use centimeters and measure to the nearest tenth. Olivia can wash a car in 3 hours. George can wash a car in 4 hours. How long will it take them working together to wash one car?

5. Triangles that have the same shape are called *similar triangles*. You may have learned that corresponding sides of similar triangles form equal ratios. Using the drawing at the top of the page, you can thus conclude that Equations A and B below are true. Use the equations to prove the formula for the work problem.

Equation A	**Equation B**	**Work Formula**
$\dfrac{z}{x} = \dfrac{n}{m + n}$	$\dfrac{z}{y} = \dfrac{m}{m + n}$	$\dfrac{1}{x} + \dfrac{1}{y} = \dfrac{1}{z}$

14 **Chapter 14 Test, Form 1**

Assessment

Write the letter for the correct answer in the blank at the right of each question.

1. A basketball team uses red or white jerseys and red or white shorts. Which tree diagram shows the possible uniforms the team can wear?

   A. Jersey   Shorts   Outcomes

   R ⟨ R —— RR / W —— RW

   W ⟨ R —— WR / W —— WW

   B. Red   White   Outcomes

   J —— S —— JS

   S —— J —— SJ

   C. Clothes   Color   Outcomes

   J ⟨ R —— JR / W —— JW

   S ⟨ R —— SR / W —— SW

   D. Color   Clothes   Outcomes

   R ⟨ J —— RJ / S —— RS

   W ⟨ J —— WJ / S —— WS

   1. _____

2. Two dice are rolled. How many outcomes are possible?
   A. 2   **B.** 36   **C.** 30   **D.** 6

   2. _____

For Questions 3 and 4, evaluate each expression. Choose each answer from:
   A. 20   **B.** 21   **C.** 10   **D.** 42

   3. _____

3. $_7P_2$

4. $_5C_2$

   4. _____

5. How many ways can 4 chairs be filled by 6 children if order is important?
   A. 360   **B.** 720   **C.** 15   **D.** 12

   5. _____

6. How many ways can a committee of 4 people be chosen from a group of 8 people if the members are selected in no particular order?
   A. 840   **B.** 70   **C.** 28   **D.** 35

   6. _____

For Questions 7–9, a bag contains 2 blue chips, 4 green chips, and 3 white chips. Find each probability. Choose each answer from:
   A. $\frac{1}{12}$ **B.** $\frac{2}{3}$ **C.** $\frac{8}{81}$ **D.** $\frac{7}{9}$

7. randomly drawing a blue chip, replacing it, then drawing a green chip

   7. _____

8. randomly selecting a green or white chip on the first draw

   8. _____

9. randomly selecting 2 white chips without replacement

   9. _____

10. A card is randomly drawn from a standard deck of cards. What is the probability that it is a two or a heart?
    A. $\frac{4}{13}$ **B.** $\frac{17}{52}$ **C.** $\frac{1}{26}$ **D.** $\frac{2}{13}$

    10. _____

11. A store sells shirts with 3 designs and 4 colors. How many different shirts are possible if there is only 1 design and 1 color per shirt?
    A. 7   **B.** 12   **C.** 4   **D.** 24

    11. _____

The table shows the attendance of 300 ninth graders over the past month.
Choose each answer from:

A. $\frac{11}{60}$ **B.** $\frac{2}{5}$

C. $\frac{17}{30}$ **D.** $\frac{1}{4}$

Number of Absences	Number of Students
0	50
1	120
2	75
3 or more	55

12. Find the probability that a randomly-chosen ninth grader will be absent 2 days next month.

12. _____

13. Find the probability that a randomly-chosen ninth grader will be absent fewer than 2 days next month.

13. _____

The table shows the probability distribution for the data used in Questions 12 and 13. Choose each answer from:

A. 0.82   **B.** 0.57

C. 0.43   **D.** 0.83

X = Number of Absences	Probability
0	0.17
1	0.40
2	0.25
3 or more	0.18

14. What is the probability that a ninth-grade student has fewer than 2 absences in a month?

14. _____

15. What is the probability that a ninth-grade student will have at least 1 absence in a month?

15. _____

For Questions 16 and 17, the table shows the number of heads and tails that occurred in 50 tosses of a coin. Choose each answer from:

Heads	Tails
22	28

A. $\frac{14}{25}$ **B.** $\frac{11}{25}$ **C.** $\frac{1}{2}$ **D.** 1

16. Based on these results, what is the probability that a coin toss results in a head?

16. _____

17. What is the theoretical probability that a coin toss results in a head?

17. _____

18. A clown has 5 balloons. How many different ways are there to give away 3 balloons?

    A. 60   **B.** 6   **C.** 120   **D.** 10

18. _____

What could you use to simulate the outcome of each event. Choose each answer from:

    A. drawing a marble from a bag of 3 white marbles and 2 black marbles

    B. using a spinner with 75% of the spinner white and 25% black

    C. rolling a die and using only 3 numbers

    D. tossing a coin twice

19. picking a novel from a shelf that contains 3 novels and 2 biographies

19. _____

20. having rain or no rain on a day when the probability of rain is 75%

20. _____

Bonus Two people are each asked to randomly choose a red, yellow, or blue marble from a bag with replacement. Use a tree diagram to find the outcomes in the sample space. What is the probability they choose the same color?

B: _____

Chapter 14 Test, Form 2A

Write the letter for the correct answer in the blank at the right of each question.

1. **DINING** A deli has a special. You can choose rye bread or onion rolls, turkey or vegetarian, and swiss or jack cheese. If you drew a tree diagram for the sample space, which would be a list of outcomes?
   A. ROTVSJ
   B. RS, RJ, OS, OJ, TS, TJ, VS, VJ
   C. RTS, RTJ, RVS, RVJ, OTS, OTJ, OVS, OVJ
   D. RTVS, RTVJ, OTVS, OTVJ   1. _____

2. How many ways can 6 different bicycles be lined up in a bike rack?
   A. 6   B. 720   C. 30   D. 21   2. _____

3. How many different vehicles are possible if you choose one each of 2 transmissions, 7 body styles, and 4 engines?
   A. 13   B. 22   C. 28   D. 56   3. _____

For Exercises 4 and 5, evaluate the expression. Choose each answer from:

   A. 715   B. 151,200   C. 17,160   D. 210   4. _____

4. $_{10}P_6$ 5. $_{13}C_4$ 5. _____

6. In how many ways can the top six seeds (rankings) be chosen from nine players on a tennis team?
   A. 362,880   B. 720   C. 60,480   D. 84   6. _____

7. How many different groups of 6 shirts can be formed from 10 shirts for a display?
   A. 210   B. 60   C. 16   D. 151,200   7. _____

8. How many different combinations of three books can be selected from 40 books?
   A. 59,280   B. 42   C. 80   D. 9880   8. _____

For Questions 9–11, there are 15 cherry, 17 grape, and 14 orange juice boxes in the cooler. Find each probability. Choose each answer from:

   A. $\frac{105}{1058}$ B. $\frac{119}{1058}$ C. $\frac{136}{1035}$ D. $\frac{29}{46}$

9. randomly selecting two grape juice boxes without replacement   9. _____

10. randomly selecting a grape juice box, replacing it, then selecting an orange one   10. _____

11. randomly selecting a cherry or orange juice box   11. _____

12. **LIBRARIES** There are 10 novels and 15 hardback books on a shelf. Seven of the 10 novels are paperback books. If there are 32 books on the shelf, what is the probability that a randomly-chosen book is a novel or a hardback book?
   A. $\frac{11}{16}$ B. $\frac{25}{32}$ C. $\frac{9}{16}$ D. 1   12. _____

The table shows the number of books students carry in their book bags.
Choose each answer from:

A. $\frac{12}{13}$ **B.** $\frac{37}{52}$

C. $\frac{13}{20}$ **D.** $\frac{47}{130}$

Number of Books	Number of Students
0	8
1	23
2	60
3	94
4 or more	75

13. Find the probability that a randomly-chosen student has exactly 3 books in his or her book bag.

13. _____

14. Find the probability that a randomly-chosen student has fewer than 4 books in his or her book bag.

14. _____

The table shows the probability distribution for the data used in
Questions 13 and 14. Choose each answer from:

A. 0.59 **B.** 0.65

C. 0.88 **D.** 0.29

X = Number of Books	Probability
0	0.03
1	0.09
2	0.23
3	0.36
4 or more	0.29

15. What is the probability that a student has 3 or more books in his or her book bag?

15. _____

16. What is the probability that a student has 2 or 3 books in his or her book bag?

16. _____

The table shows the results of tossing
two coins 50 times.

Outcomes	H, H	H, T	T, H	T, T
Frequency	10	15	12	13

17. Based on these results, what is the probability that two coins tossed results in two tails?

A. $\frac{13}{50}$ **B.** $\frac{3}{10}$ **C.** $\frac{6}{25}$ **D.** $\frac{4}{5}$

17. _____

18. How many of the next 60 tosses should result in two tails?

A. 12 **B.** 32 **C.** 16 **D.** 14

18. _____

What could you use to simulate the outcome of each event?
Choose each answer from:

A. tossing a coin 4 times

B. drawing, without replacement, from a bag that contains 4 marbles, each a different color

C. using a spinner divided into 4 equal parts

D. rolling a die 4 times

19. eating at a restaurant two nights in a row, then eating at home two nights in a row when eating in a restaurant and eating at home are equally likely.

19. _____

20. results of a 4-person race if each of the 4 people are equally likely to win

20. _____

Bonus Find n so that $_nC_3 = {_nP_2}$.

B: _____

14 # Chapter 14 Test, Form 2B

Assessment

Write the letter for the correct answer in the blank at right of each question.

1. **DINING** A cafe has a salad special. You can choose lettuce or spinach, chicken or egg, and Italian or Thousand Island dressing. If you drew a tree diagram for the sample space, which would be a list of the outcomes?
   A. LSCEIT
   B. LCI, LCT, LEI, LET, SCI, SCT, SEI, SET
   C. LI, LT, SI, ST, EI, ET
   D. LCI, LET, SCI, LST

1. _____

2. How many ways can Oscar list his first, second, and third choices from a list of 12 books for summer reading?
   A. 36   **B.** 1728   **C.** 33   **D.** 1320

2. _____

3. How many different birthday cakes are possible if you choose one each of 3 sizes, 6 flavors, and 4 designs?
   A. 72   **B.** 13   **C.** 30   **D.** 36

3. _____

For Exercises 4 and 5, evaluate the expression. Choose each answer from:
   A. 990   **B.** 792   **C.** 165   **D.** 95,040

4. _____

4. $_{11}P_3$ 5. $_{12}C_5$

5. _____

6. In how many ways can the first 5 places be decided from 12 players in a golf tournament?
   A. 120   **B.** 60   **C.** 3,991,680   **D.** 95,040

6. _____

7. How many groups of 5 CDs can be chosen from 10 different CDs?
   A. 30,240   **B.** 50   **C.** 252   **D.** 15

7. _____

8. How many different ways can 4 rolls of film be selected from 50 rolls?
   A. 230,300   **B.** 100   **C.** 54   **D.** 5,527,200

8. _____

For Questions 9–11, there are 16 black socks, 9 blue socks, and 15 brown socks mixed in a drawer. Find each probability. Choose each answer from:

   A. $\frac{3}{5}$ **B.** $\frac{7}{52}$ **C.** $\frac{9}{100}$ **D.** $\frac{135}{256}$

9. randomly selecting a black sock, replacing it, then selecting a blue sock

9. _____

10. randomly selecting two brown socks without replacement

10. _____

11. randomly selecting a blue or brown sock

11. _____

12. **SCHOOL** There are 10 girls in Lisann's math class and 12 students that are also in her science class. Six of the 10 girls are not in her science class. If 26 students are in the math class, what is the probability that a randomly-chosen student is a girl or is also in Lisann's science class?
   A. $\frac{11}{13}$ **B.** 1   **C.** $\frac{8}{13}$ **D.** $\frac{9}{13}$

12. _____

The table shows the number of stores each mall customer has visited. Choose each answer from:

A. $\frac{22}{35}$ **B.** $\frac{17}{140}$

C. $\frac{8}{35}$ **D.** $\frac{3}{5}$

Number of Stores	Number of Customers
0	8
1	22
2	34
3	112
4 or more	104

13. Find the probability that a randomly-chosen customer has visited exactly 2 stores.

13. _____

14. Find the probability that a randomly-chosen customer has visited fewer than 4 stores.

14. _____

The table shows the probability distribution for the data used in Questions 13 and 14. Choose each answer from:

A. 0.771 **B.** 0.229
C. 0.371 **D.** 0.108

X = Number of Stores	Probability
0	0.029
1	0.079
2	0.121
3	0.400
4 or more	0.371

15. What is the probability that a customer has visited fewer than 2 stores?

15. _____

16. What is the probability that a customer has visited 3 or more stores?

16. _____

The table shows the results of tossing two coins 50 times.

Outcomes	H, H	H, T	T, H	T, T
Frequency	16	11	9	14

17. Based on these results, what is the probability that two coins tossed result in two heads?

A. $\frac{8}{25}$ **B.** $\frac{2}{5}$ **C.** $\frac{18}{25}$ **D.** $\frac{7}{25}$

17. _____

18. How many of the next 40 tosses should result in two heads?

A. 16 **B.** 13 **C.** 11 **D.** 29

18. _____

What could you use to simulate the outcome of each event? Choose each answer from:

A. using a spinner divided into 5 equal parts

B. tossing a coin 5 times

C. drawing, without replacement, from a bag of 5 marbles, each a different color

D. rolling a die 5 times

19. going to a park three days in a row, then staying at home two days in a row when going to a park and staying home are equally likely.

19. _____

20. the results of a spelling bee with 5 participants if each of the people are equally likely to win

20. _____

Bonus Find n so that $_nP_4 = {}_{n+1}P_3$.

B: _____

Assessment

14   **Chapter 14 Test, Form 2C**   SCORE _____

For Questions 1 and 2, use a tree diagram to find the sample space for each event. List the possible outcomes.

1. tossing a nickel then tossing a dime

1. _____

2. buying soap that is made for 3 skin types (dry, normal, oily), in both scented and unscented formulas

2. _____

3. A sofa is manufactured in 3 styles, 2 sizes, and 10 fabrics. How many different sofas are possible?

3. _____

4. Three students are running for president, 7 for vice-president, and 5 for treasurer. How many different ways can the offices be filled?

4. _____

5. _____

For Questions 5 and 6, evaluate each expression.

5. $_{14}C_4$ **6.** $_{15}P_3$

6. _____

7. A volleyball team has 6 players. How many different teams can be formed from 12 people if position doesn't matter?

7. _____

8. Ten people are riding horses on a trail. If the riders must stay in single file, how many ways can the first 4 positions be filled?

8. _____

For Questions 9 and 10, there are 12 orange golf balls, 14 yellow golf balls, and 15 white golf balls in the bottom of a golf bag. Find each probability.

9. randomly selecting two yellow golf balls without replacement

9. _____

10. randomly selecting an orange golf ball or a white golf ball

10. _____

11. Two dice are tossed. What is the probability of getting an even number on one die and a number less than 3 on the other?

11. _____

12. A card is randomly drawn from a standard deck of cards. What is the probability that the card drawn is a king or a diamond?

12. _____

The owner of a barber shop asked customers how many hair cuts they received in a 3-month period. The results are shown in the table.

13. Find the probability that a randomly-chosen customer had 3 haircuts in the 3-month period.

13. _____

14. Find the probability that a randomly-chosen customer had fewer than 3 hair cuts in the 3-month period.

14. _____

Number of Hair Cuts	Number of Customers
1	14
2	20
3	45
4	33

Chapter 14 Test, Form 2C *(continued)*

The owner of a travel agency asked customers how many flights they had taken in a 1-year period. The table shows the results written as a probability distribution.

15. Show that the probability distribution is valid.

16. What is the probability that a randomly-chosen customer had 3 or more flights in the 1-year period?

X = Number of Flights	Probability
0	0.264
1	0.087
2	0.223
3	0.162
4	0.203
5 or more	0.061

15. _____

16. _____

For Questions 17 and 18, a teacher recently gave her 50 algebra students a 5-question quiz. The table shows the number of students who answered each question correctly.

17. Based on the data, what is the probability that a student from this class answered question number 3 correctly?

18. Using the data, how many of the 120 algebra students at the school who are taught algebra by other teachers would you expect to answer question number 3 correctly?

Question Number	Number Correct
1	45
2	15
3	32
4	40
5	29

17. _____

18. _____

19. MOVIES A ticket counter has 4 different booths that are fed by a common line, with the fourth booth serving 3 times as many customers as each of the other booths. What could be used for a simulation to determine the probability of being served by 1 of the 4 booths?

19. _____

20. FISHING Set-su is equally likely to fish in each of 6 streams near her home. To simulate this situation, she rolls a die 75 times and records the number rolled. The table shows the results, with each number representing a different stream. Based on her results, what is the probability that she fishes in the fourth stream on her next fishing trip?

20. _____

1	2	3	4	5	6
11	13	12	15	14	10

Bonus Evaluate $(4!)(_{10}C_5)$.

B: _____

Chapter 14 Test, Form 2D SCORE _____

For Questions 1 and 2, use a tree diagram to find the sample space for each event. List the possible outcomes.

1. drawing a marble from a bag containing a red and a blue marble and tossing a coin

1. _____

2. buying shoes that come in 2 styles (loafer and tie) and 3 colors (black, gray, and white)

2. _____

3. Photographs can be ordered in 6 sizes, on 4 types of paper, and with 3 types of finish. How many different photographs are possible?

3. _____

4. Five students are running for president, 6 for vice-president, and 4 for secretary. How many different ways can the offices be filled?

4. _____

5. _____

For Questions 5 and 6, evaluate each expression.

5. $_{12}C_3$ 6. $_{16}P_5$

6. _____

7. A basketball team has 5 players. How many different teams can be formed from 15 people if position doesn't matter?

7. _____

8. Eight people are hiking a trail in a single file formation. How many ways can the first 5 positions be filled?

8. _____

For Questions 9 and 10, Saul received a tub of dinosaurs that had 16 brachiosaurs, 15 triceratops, and 7 tyrannosaurs. Find each probability.

9. randomly selecting two triceratops without replacement

9. _____

10. randomly selecting a brachiosaurus or a tyrannosaurus

10. _____

11. Two dice are rolled. What is the probability of getting a number greater than two on one die and a 1 or 6 on the other?

11. _____

12. A card is randomly drawn from a standard deck of cards. What is the probability that the card is a heart or a 10?

12. _____

A survey asked homeowners how many televisions they have in their home. The results are shown in the table.

13. Find the probability that a randomly-chosen home owner has 1 television in their home.

13. _____

14. Find the probability that a randomly-chosen homeowner has more than 2 televisions in their home.

14. _____

Number of Televisions	Number of Homeowners
1	42
2	38
3	25
4 or more	11

Glencoe Algebra 1

14 **Chapter 14 Test, Form 2D** *(continued)*

The owner of a shoe store asked customers how many pairs of shoes they had bought in a 6-month period. The table shows the results written as a probability distribution.

15. Show that the probability distribution is valid.

16. What is the probability that a randomly-chosen customer bought 4 or more pairs of shoes in the 6-month period?

X = Number of Pairs of Shoes	Probability
0	0.027
1	0.213
2	0.384
3	0.203
4	0.123
5 or more	0.050

15. _____

16. _____

For Questions 17 and 18, the student council recently surveyed 500 students to determine what activities are most popular for spirit week. The table shows the number of votes for each activity.

17. Based on the chart, what is the probability that a student from this group voted for a dance?

18. How many of the 1400 students who did not take the survey would you expect to vote for a dance?

Activity	Number of Votes
Dance	310
Rally	425
Costume Contest	400
Class Competition	270

17. _____

18. _____

19. **TRANSPORTATION** Three taxicab companies provide service from a local mall. The first company has 4 times as many cabs as each of the other 2 companies. What could be used for a simulation determining the probability of being served by 1 of the 3 companies?

19. _____

20. **BREAKFAST** Esteban is equally likely to select one of six cereals for breakfast. To simulate this situation, he rolls a die 75 times and records the number rolled. The table shows the results, with each number representing a different cereal. Based on his results, what is the probability that he selects cereal 3 at his next breakfast?

1	2	3	4	5	6
12	14	10	15	11	13

20. _____

Bonus Evaluate $\dfrac{_{10}P_5}{4!}$.

B: _____

14 Chapter 14 Test, Form 3

For Questions 1 and 2, use a tree diagram to find the sample space for each event. List possible outcomes.

1. buying a nonfat frozen yogurt with a choice of vanilla or berry yogurt, toppings of almonds or walnuts, in a sugar cone, plain cone, or dish

   1. _____

2. tossing a dime once and selecting a marble from a bag that contains 1 green, 1 red, 1 blue, and 1 orange marble

   2. _____

3. How many ways can the nine student council members arrange themselves in a row on stage during an assembly?

   3. _____

4. **LANDSCAPING** When landscaping her yard, Jessica had a choice of 5 trees, 6 flowering shrubs, and 4 groundcovers. How many ways can she choose a tree, a flowering shrub, a groundcover, and then another tree to plant in that order?

   4. _____

For Questions 5 and 6, evaluate each expression.

5. $\frac{_{12}C_6}{_{14}P_2}$

6. $(_6C_3)(_9P_2)$

   5. _____

   6. _____

7. A band is going on tour to promote the 12 songs on their new album. If they play only 7 songs, how many ways can they arrange 7 songs for their performance?

   7. _____

8. **EDUCATION** If 6 science fair exhibits are chosen at random from 4 biology, 7 chemistry, and 9 physics exhibits to go to the county finals, what is the probability that there will be 2 from each subject area?

   8. _____

For Questions 9 and 10, a bag contains 16 blue marbles, 17 red marbles, and 13 orange marbles. Two marbles are randomly drawn from the bag and not replaced. Find each probability if the marbles are drawn in the order indicated.

9. P(blue, not red)

   9. _____

10. P(red, not orange)

   10. _____

11. What is the probability that a card randomly drawn from a standard deck is less than 5 or a heart or a diamond? (Assume aces are less than 5.)

   11. _____

12. **VEHICLES** A car dealer has 106 vehicles of which 48 are new, 42 are trucks, and 32 are red. If there are 6 used, red trucks and 12 new red vehicles, what is the probability of choosing a new or red vehicle?

   12. _____

14   **Chapter 14 Test, Form 3** *(continued)*

**Suppose a die is rolled. Let the random variable *X*
represent the number of rolls until the result is a 6.**

13. Calculate the probability distribution for $X = 1, 2$, and 3.

13. _____

14. Find the probability that the die will be rolled more than
3 times.

14. _____

**The table shows the probability distribution of the number
of islands visited by visitors to the Hawaiian Islands.**

15. How many of 190 visitors are
expected to visit more than
3 islands?

X = Number of Islands	Probability
1	0.483
2	0.175
3	0.197
4 or more	0.145

15. _____

16. What is the probability that a
visitor does not visit exactly
3 islands?

16. _____

**For Questions 17 and 18, the owner of a gym surveyed
165 customers to find out what days each customer used
the gym. The table shows part of the results.**

17. What is the probability that
a customer uses the gym on
Monday?

Day	Number of Customers
Monday	124
Wednesday	119
Friday	18

17. _____

18. How many of the 592 people who
have memberships are expected
to use the gym on Fridays?

18. _____

19. A hotel has 12 different conference rooms and
3 different kitchens. What could be used for a simulation
determining the probability that a dinner is served in one
of the conference rooms and cooked in one of the kitchens?

19. _____

20. **JOBS** Each of 3 friends is equally likely to go to a career
fair or stay home. To simulate this situation, they toss 3 coins
80 times and record the results, with heads representing
going to the career fair and tails representing staying home.
What is the probability that more than one of the friends
goes to the career fair?

20. _____

HHH	HHT	HTH	THH	TTH	THT	HTT	TTT
12	9	6	12	10	12	9	10

Bonus There are 5 girls and 6 boys on a student government
committee. A subcommittee of 5 people is being selected
to plan the activities. What is the probability that the
subcommittee will have at least 3 girls?

B: _____

14 **Chapter 14 Open-Ended Assessment** SCORE _____

Demonstrate your knowledge by giving a clear, concise solution to each problem. Be sure to include all relevant drawings and justify your answers. You may show your solution in more than one way or investigate beyond the requirements of the problem.

1. Determine if the use of the word *combination* in the phrases given matches the mathematical definition. Then, decide if the word *combination* should be replaced by the word *permutation*, and explain your reasoning.

   a. a combination lock on a bicycle

   b. a combination plate on a menu

   c. a combination shot in a pool game

   d. a winning combination

2. **BUSINESS** Nora wants to open a computer business. She prepares a survey to help her determine the use of computers in her community. She asks questions concerning 4 topics: the type of computer owned, the number of computers owned, the type of software owned, and the number of hours per day the computers are in use.

   a. Write 2 questions that would fit in any of the 4 topics and describe possible events that would be an example of independent or dependent events and an example of mutually exclusive or inclusive events.

   b. Write a question for one of the topics and use a random variable with at least 3 categories to represent the possible outcomes. Make a table that shows 50 possible results. Make a probability distribution from the results contained in the table.

3. For each event, explain whether the probability is an experimental or theoretical probability.

   a. A card is drawn from a standard deck of cards. $P(7) = \frac{4}{13}$.

   b. Out of a group of 150 people, 62 people are wearing black shoes. The probability that a person wears black shoes is $\frac{31}{75}$.

4. **a.** Describe an event that can be simulated by tossing a coin.

   b. Describe an event that can be simulated by tossing two coins.

5. Use only the notation $_nP_r$, $r!$, and $_nC_r$ to write an equation. Then, give values for n and r to illustrate your equation.

14 **Chapter 14 Vocabulary Test/Review** SCORE _____

combination	experimental	independent events	random variable
complements	probability	mutually exclusive	relative frequency
compound event	factorial	network	sample space
dependent events	finite graph	node	simulation
edge	Fundamental	permutation	theoretical probability
empirical study	Counting Principle	probability distribution	traceable
event	inclusive	probability histogram	tree diagram

Choose from the terms above to complete each sentence.

1. In an experiment, any specific outcome is called an _____.

2. The expression $6 \cdot 5 \cdot 4 \cdot 3 \cdot 2 \cdot 1$ can be written as 6! using

_____ notation.

3. Multiplying the number of choices for each position in a 4-digit

ID number is an illustration of the _____.

4. A method used for counting the number of possible outcomes is

to draw a _____.

5. A list of all possible outcomes is called the _____.

6. The events for rolling a 6 on a die and not rolling a 6 on a die

are called _____.

7. A _____ is a variable whose value is the numerical
outcome of a random event.

8. A _____ is a type of graph used to illustrate the
probability distribution for a random variable.

9. _____ is the number of times an outcome occurred.

10. Performing an experiment repeatedly, collecting and combining the data,

and analyzing the results is known as an _____.

In your own words—
Define each term.

11. probability distribution

12. compound event

14 **Chapter 14 Quiz**
(Lessons 14–1 and 14–2)

SCORE _____

Use a tree diagram to find the sample space for each event. List the possible outcomes.

1. making a sundae from chocolate or vanilla ice cream, and fudge, butterscotch, or strawberry topping

2. tossing a penny, dime, and nickel

For Questions 3 and 4, find the value of each expression.

3. 5!   4. 12!

5. How many different meals are possible if you choose one each of 5 sandwiches, 4 drinks, and 2 desserts?

Determine whether each situation involves a *permutation* or *combination*. Explain your reasoning.

6. first and second place winners in a basketball tournament

7. a selection of 2 CDs from a group of 8

For Questions 8 and 9, evaluate each expression.

8. $_{10}P_4$ 9. $_8C_2$

10. **STANDARDIZED TEST PRACTICE** A club with 42 members has to choose a president, vice-president and treasurer. In how many ways can this be done?
    A. 1   **B.** 14   **C.** 11,480   **D.** 68,880

1. _____

2. _____

3. _____

4. _____

5. _____

6. _____

7. _____

8. _____

9. _____

10. _____

- -

14 **Chapter 14 Quiz**
(Lesson 14–3)

SCORE _____

A jar contains 5 red and 3 black marbles. Find each probability.

1. randomly drawing a red marble, replacing it, then randomly drawing a black marble

2. randomly selecting two black marbles without replacement

A card is randomly drawn from a standard deck of cards. Find each probability.

3. P(10 or Jack)   4. P(heart or 5)

5. P(red or less than 5)   (Assume aces are less than 5.)

1. _____

2. _____

3. _____

4. _____

5. _____

14 # Chapter 14 Quiz

(Lesson 14–4)

The table shows the possible differences when rolling two dice and the number of ways each difference can be found.

Difference of Two Dice	0	1	2	3	4	5
Ways to Achieve Difference	6	10	8	6	4	2

1. Show in a table the sample space of all possible outcomes.

2. Find the probability distribution for $X = 2$, $X = 3$, and $X = 4$.

3. What is the probability that the difference of the dice is less than 3 on two separate rolls?

1. _____

2. _____

3. _____

The table shows the probability distribution of the income in dollars per household in the United States in 2000.

4. Find the probability that a household made $50,000 or more in 2000.

5. Based on the probability distribution, how many of 50 households chosen at random made less than $75,000 in 2000?

X = Income per Household	Probability
Less than $25,000	0.30
$25,000–$49,999	0.29
$50,000–$74,999	0.19
$75,000–$99,999	0.10
$100,000 or more	0.12

4. _____

5. _____

- -

14 # Chapter 14 Quiz

(Lesson 14–5)

The table shows the results of a survey on family sizes.

1. Find the probability distribution for households with 1, 2, and 3 family members.

2. What is the probability that a family chosen at random has 3 or more family members?

Number of Family Members	Number of Households
1	210
2	300
3	516
4 or more	534

1. _____

2. _____

How could you simulate the outcomes of the situations?

3. a person choosing 1 of 6 lines at the grocery store

4. a student using 1 of 4 pencil sharpeners in a classroom

5. a family having 2 girls and 1 boy

3. _____

4. _____

5. _____

14 Chapter 14 Mid-Chapter Test

SCORE _____

(Lessons 14–1 through 14–3)

Part I *Write the letter for the correct answer in the blank at right of each question.*

1. How many different class schedules are possible if a student picks one each of 3 math classes, 2 science classes, and 5 PE classes?

A. 10   **B.** 1   **C.** 21   **D.** 30   1. _____

2. Evaluate $_{10}P_4$.

A. 5040   **B.** 40   **C.** 210   **D.** 6   2. _____

3. A science class must choose 5 out of 16 science projects to advance to the county competition. How many different groups of projects could be selected?

A. 3   **B.** 4368   **C.** 524,160   **D.** 80   3. _____

4. A box contains 5 yellow, 4 red, 2 blue, and 6 brown cubes. Once a cube is selected it is not replaced. Find P(yellow, then brown).

A. $\dfrac{25}{289}$ **B.** $\dfrac{15}{136}$ **C.** $\dfrac{1}{3}$ **D.** $\dfrac{25}{272}$ 4. _____

5. A die is rolled and a coin is tossed. Find P(6 and heads).

A. $\dfrac{1}{12}$ **B.** $\dfrac{1}{6}$ **C.** $\dfrac{1}{8}$ **D.** $\dfrac{2}{3}$ 5. _____

Part II

6. If the first digit of a 3-digit number cannot be 0, how many 3-digit numbers are possible?

6. _____

7. From a collection of 9 books, Martin is asked to list his 5 favorites starting with his most favorite, second favorite, third favorite, and so on. How many ways can Martin make his list?

7. _____

8. Evaluate $_{14}C_{10}$.

8. _____

9. In an assortment of calculators, 12 are graphing calculators, 16 are scientific calculators, and 7 are business calculators. Find the probability of randomly selecting a business calculator, replacing it, then randomly selecting a graphing calculator.

9. _____

10. LANDSCAPING A town recently surveyed 500 residents to determine how many residents would recycle. 225 residents said they would recycle paper products, 190 residents said they would recycle glass, and of these residents 180 residents said they would recycle both paper and glass. What is the probability that a randomly-chosen resident who took part in the survey will recycle glass or paper?

10. _____

11. _____

11. A family has 3 children. Draw a tree diagram to show the sample space. How many different outcomes are possible?

14 Chapter 14 Cumulative Review
(Chapters 1–14)

1. Find the next three items in the sequence $\dfrac{1}{32}, \dfrac{1}{16}, \dfrac{1}{8}, \dfrac{1}{4}, \ldots$ (Lesson 4–8)

1. _____

2. Use elimination to solve the system of equations. (Lesson 7–3)
   $-9x - 3y = 24$
   $-5x + 3y = 4$

2. _____

3. Find $(2a - 3b^2)^2$. (Lesson 8–8)

3. _____

4. Find the GCF of $60a^3bc^2$ and $42abc^4$. (Lesson 9–1)

4. _____

5. Solve $x - 1 = \sqrt{x + 1}$. (Lesson 11–3)

5. _____

6. Find $\dfrac{m^2 + 5m + 6}{m + 4} \div \dfrac{m + 2}{m^2 + 5m + 4}$. (Lesson 12–4)

6. _____

7. Simplify $\dfrac{x - \dfrac{x + 4}{x - 3}}{\dfrac{x + 4}{x - 3} + x}$ (Lesson 12–8)

7. _____

8. State the dimensions of the matrix. Then, identify the position of the circled element. (Lesson 13–2)
   $\begin{bmatrix} -7 & 9 & ⑤ \\ 2 & 0 & -6 \end{bmatrix}$

8. _____

For Questions 9 and 10, use the histogram that shows the number of pets in some households.

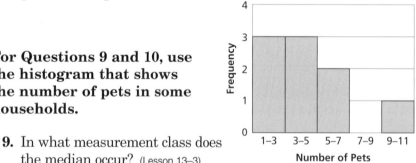

9. In what measurement class does the median occur? (Lesson 13–3)

9. _____

10. Describe the distribution of the data. (Lesson 13–3)

10. _____

11. How many different outcomes are there for the number of boys and girls in a family with 4 children? (Lesson 14–1)

11. _____

12. How many different committees of 3 people can be chosen from the 100 members of the U.S. Senate? (Lesson 14–2)

12. _____

13. A card is selected at random from a standard deck of cards. What is the probability that the card drawn is a king or a club? (Lesson 14–3)

13. _____

14 # Standardized Test Practice
(Chapters 1–14)

Part 1: Multiple Choice

Instructions: Fill in the appropriate oval for the best answer.

1. What is the next term in the arithmetic sequence $a + 1.7$, $a + 2.8$, $a + 3.9$, $a + 5$, …? (Lesson 4–7)

   A. $a + 6$ **B.** $a + 6.1$ **C.** $a + 7$ **D.** $a + 1.7$ **1.** Ⓐ Ⓑ Ⓒ Ⓓ

2. A pasture is estimated to produce 200 kilogram of fodder (food for grazing). A 450-kilogram beef cow requires 11.8 kilogram of fodder per day. Which equation represents the amount of fodder f left in the pasture after one 450-kilogram cow has been grazing d days? (Lesson 5–4)

   E. $d = -11.8f + 450$ **F.** $d = 11.8f + 200$

   G. $f = 450d$ **H.** $f = -11.8d + 200$ **2.** Ⓔ Ⓕ Ⓖ Ⓗ

3. Find $(x^2 - 3x + 2) - (3x^2 + 5x + 7)$. (Lesson 8–5)

   A. $-2x^2 - 8x - 5$ **B.** $2x^2 + 8x + 5$

   C. $2x^2 + 2x + 5$ **D.** $-2x^2 - 2x - 5$ **3.** Ⓐ Ⓑ Ⓒ Ⓓ

4. Which trinomial is *not* a perfect square trinomial? (Lesson 10–3)

   E. $x^2 + 42x + 441$ **F.** $x^2 - 28x + 196$

   G. $x^2 - 34x + 374$ **H.** $x^2 + 30x + 225$ **4.** Ⓔ Ⓕ Ⓖ Ⓗ

5. Which side measures form a right triangle? (Lesson 11–4)

   A. $16, 30, 33$ **B.** $18, 19, 26$ **C.** $9, 23, 24$ **D.** $20, 21, 29$ **5.** Ⓐ Ⓑ Ⓒ Ⓓ

6. What is the quotient of $14b^3 + b^2 - 10b + 3$ divided by $7b - 3$? (Lesson 12–5)

   E. $2b^2 + b - 1$ **F.** $2b^2 + b - \dfrac{13}{7} + \dfrac{6}{7b - 3}$

   G. $2b^2 - \dfrac{5}{7}b - 2$ **H.** $2b^2 - b + 10$ **6.** Ⓔ Ⓕ Ⓖ Ⓗ

7. Find $6A$ if $A = \begin{bmatrix} 4 & 0 & -5 \\ -2 & 3 & 1 \end{bmatrix}$. (Lesson 13–2)

   A. $\begin{bmatrix} 10 & 6 & 1 \\ 4 & 9 & 9 \end{bmatrix}$ **B.** $\begin{bmatrix} -24 & 6 & 30 \\ 4 & 18 & 7 \end{bmatrix}$

   C. $\begin{bmatrix} 24 & 0 & -30 \\ -12 & 18 & 6 \end{bmatrix}$ **D.** $\begin{bmatrix} 10 & 0 & 1 \\ -12 & 9 & 6 \end{bmatrix}$ **7.** Ⓐ Ⓑ Ⓒ Ⓓ

8. Max wants to read his four favorite books again. In how many different ways can he read the four books? (Lesson 14–1)

   E. 10 **F.** 4 **G.** 24 **H.** 12 **8.** Ⓔ Ⓕ Ⓖ Ⓗ

9. A bag contains 5 red marbles, 4 blue marbles, and 8 green marbles. Three marbles are randomly drawn from the bag and not replaced. Find $P(\text{red}, \text{green}, \textit{not} \text{ blue})$. (Lesson 14–3)

   A. $\dfrac{440}{4913}$ **B.** $\dfrac{11}{102}$ **C.** $\dfrac{779}{510}$ **D.** $\dfrac{2}{17}$ **9.** Ⓐ Ⓑ Ⓒ Ⓓ

14 **Standardized Test Practice** *(continued)*

Part 2: Grid In

Instructions: Enter your answer by writing each digit of the answer in a column box and then shading in the appropriate oval that corresponds to that entry.

10. If $f(x) = x^2 + 4x - 5$, find $f(-8)$. (Lesson 4–6)

11. Solve $\sqrt{2x + 1} - 3 = 4$. (Lesson 11–3)

12. Daniel can plant an acre of corn in 6 hours. Working with Amanda, they can plant an acre of corn in 2 hours. How long would it take in hours for Amanda to plant an acre of corn by herself? (Lesson 12–9)

13. Find $_9P_4$. (Lesson 14–2)

10.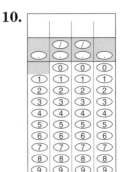

11.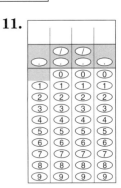

12.

13.

Part 3: Quantitative Comparison

Instructions: Compare the quantities in columns A and B. Shade in
- (A) if the quantity in column A is greater;
- (B) if the quantity in column B is greater;
- (C) if the quantities are equal; or
- (D) if the relationship cannot be determined from the information given.

Column A	Column B

14. | $\sqrt{x}$ | x |

(Lesson 2–7)

14. (A) (B) (C) (D)

15. $$y = C(1 + r)^t$$

| the value of y when $C = 100$, $r = 0.15$, and $t = 8$ | the value of y when $C = 100$, $r = 0.12$, and $t = 8$ |

(Lesson 10–6)

15. (A) (B) (C) (D)

16. | the excluded value for $\dfrac{n - 9}{2n - 3}$ | the excluded value for $\dfrac{2n + 1}{2n - 5}$ |

(Lesson 12–2)

16. (A) (B) (C) (D)

17. | $_7C_7$ | $_7P_7$ |

(Lesson 14–2)

17. (A) (B) (C) (D)

Unit 5 Test
(Chapters 13–14)

For Questions 1 and 2, identify each sample, suggest a population from which it was selected, and state whether it is *unbiased* or *biased*. If unbiased, classify the sample as *simple*, *stratified*, or *systematic*. If biased, classify as *convenience* or *voluntary response*.

1. A clothing manufacturer checks for defects in the clothing made by inspecting every 50th article of clothing produced.

1. _____

2. Forty shoppers outside a health food store are asked questions concerning their exercise habits.

2. _____

3. State the dimensions of the matrix. Then identify the position of the circled element in the matrix.
$$\begin{bmatrix} 3 & 0 & -6 & 4 \\ -2 & 5 & -1 & 1 \\ 4 & ⑧ & 7 & 9 \end{bmatrix}$$

3. _____

4. Find $\begin{bmatrix} 3 & -1 & 6 \\ 2 & 0 & 4 \end{bmatrix} + 3\begin{bmatrix} 1 & 4 & 0 \\ 6 & 2 & -2 \end{bmatrix}$.

4. _____

5. In what measurement class does the median occur in the histogram at the right?

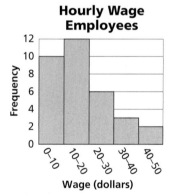

Hourly Wage Employees

5. _____

For Questions 6–9, use the data which gives the number of grams of protein in 3 ounces of different types of meat.

11 17 20 16 21 24 20 23 23 18 23 27

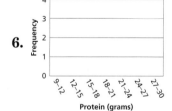

Protein Amount Per Three Ounces of Meat

6. Create a histogram to represent the data set.

6.

7. Find the median, lower quartile, and upper quartile of the set of data.

7. _____

8. Find the range and interquartile range of the set of data. Identify any outliers.

8. _____

9. Draw a box-and-whisker plot for the set of data.

9.   10 12 14 16 18 20 22 24 26 28

10. Use the parallel box-and-whisker plot to determine which set of data has the greatest interquartile range.

10. _____

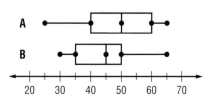

881   *Glencoe Algebra 1*

Unit 5 Test *(continued)*

11. A company sells 4 sizes of 5 different styles of sweatshirts in 6 colors. How many different sweatshirts are possible?

11. _____

12. Draw a tree diagram to show the sample space for the event of earning an A, B, or C in a Math and a Science class.

12.

13. Determine how many ways 12 songs can be ordered on a compact disk.

13. _____

14. Determine how many groups of 4 videos can be chosen from a collection of 20 videos.

14. _____

Cards are randomly drawn from a standard deck of playing cards and not replaced. Find each probability.

15. An ace and then a ten are drawn.

15. _____

16. A black card or an ace is drawn.

16. _____

The table shows the probability distribution for urban interstate speed limits in the 50 United States.

X = Speed Limit (mph)	50	55	60	65	70
Probability	0.02	0.40	0.06	0.40	0.12

17. Show that the probability distribution is valid.

17. _____

18. Find the probability that a state chosen at random has an urban interstate speed limit greater than 55 miles per hour.

18. _____

The table shows the results of tossing two coins 50 times.

Outcomes	H, H	H, T	T, H	T, T
Frequency	9	14	12	15

19. Based on these results, what is the probability that two coins tossed result in two tails?

19. _____

20. George is equally likely to walk to work each morning as he is to ride his bike. Using the results of the experiment, if heads represents riding his bike and tails represents walking, what is the probability George will ride his bike to work the next two mornings?

20. _____

Second Semester Test

(Chapters 7–14)

For Questions 1–20, write the letter for the correct answer in the blank at the right of each question.

1. How many solutions exist for the system of equations?
$3y = 2x - 4$
$6y = 4x - 8$
A. no solution **B.** one solution
C. infinitely many solutions **D.** cannot be determined **1.** _____

2. If $4x - 2y = -10$ and $3x - 2y = 10$, what is the value for y?
A. -20 **B.** -35 **C.** 45 **D.** 5 **2.** _____

3. An airplane travels 1560 miles in 3 hours flying with the wind. Flying against a wind that is the same speed, the return trip takes 4 hours. Find the rate of the plane in still air.
A. 65 mph **B.** 195 mph **C.** 455 mph **D.** 260 mph **3.** _____

4. Simplify $\frac{(2x^{-3}y^5)^0}{(4x^4y^{-2})^{-1}}$.

A. 0 **B.** $\frac{x^4}{4y^2}$ **C.** $\frac{4x^4}{y^2}$ **D.** $8xy^3$ **4.** _____

5. Solve $x(x + 2) = x^2 + x + 2$.
A. 2 **B.** 1 **C.** 0 **D.** -1 **5.** _____

6. Find $(x - y)(x + xy + y)$.
A. $x^2 + 2xy - 2xy - y^2$ **B.** $x^2 + x^2y + 2xy - xy^2 - y^2$
C. $x^2 + 2xy - y^2$ **D.** $x^2 + x^2y - xy^2 - y^2$ **6.** _____

7. Find the GCF of $48u^3v^2$ and $30uv^2$.
A. $2uv$ **B.** $6uv^2$ **C.** $12u^3v^2$ **D.** $4u^2$ **7.** _____

8. Which is a factor of $4y^2 - 6y - 4$?
A. $2y + 1$ **B.** $2y + 4$ **C.** $y + 2$ **D.** $y + 1$ **8.** _____

9. Solve $x^2 + 8x + 16 = 25$.
A. $\{4, 5\}$ **B.** $\{1, 4\}$ **C.** $\{-9, 5\}$ **D.** $\{-9, 1\}$ **9.** _____

10. Find the coordinates of the vertex of the graph of $y = -2x^2 + 12x + 17$.
A. $(-3, -37)$ **B.** $(3, 35)$ **C.** $(6, 17)$ **D.** $(0, 17)$ **10.** _____

11. Solve $3x^2 + 8 = 12x$ by using the Quadratic Formula. Round to the nearest tenth.
A. $\{-0.8, 4.8\}$ **B.** $\{1.2, 2.8\}$ **C.** $\varnothing$ **D.** $\{0.8, 3.2\}$ **11.** _____

Second Semester Test (continued)
(Chapters 7–14)

12. Determine the amount of an investment if $1000 is invested at an interest rate of 6.2% compounded monthly for 2 years.

    A. $1131.65   **B.** $2058.23   **C.** $1127.84   **D.** $4236.32   **12.** _____

13. Find $(\sqrt{6} - \sqrt{5})(\sqrt{12} + \sqrt{10})$.

    A. $4 + 3\sqrt{2}$ **B.** $\sqrt{2}$ **C.** $\sqrt{2} + 4\sqrt{15}$ **D.** $11\sqrt{2}$ **13.** _____

14. Solve $\sqrt{2x + 3} = x + 2$.

    A. -1 **B.** 1 **C.** $-\dfrac{3}{2}, -2$ **D.** no solution   **14.** _____

15. For $\triangle ABC$, find the measure of $\angle B$ to the nearest degree.

    A. 59°   **B.** 41°

    C. 49°   **D.** 31°   **15.** _____

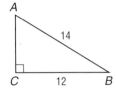

16. If y varies inversely as x and $y = 8$ when $x = 9$, find y when $x = -12$.

    A. -13 **B.** -6 **C.** 29 **D.** -4 **16.** _____

17. Find $\dfrac{n^2 - 10n + 25}{n^3} \cdot \dfrac{n}{3n - 15}$.

    A. $\dfrac{n - 5}{3n^2}$ **B.** $\dfrac{(n + 5)^2}{3n^2(n - 5)}$ **C.** $\dfrac{n^2(n - 5)}{3}$ **D.** $-\dfrac{5}{3n}$ **17.** _____

18. Two airplanes leave a city at the same time. One airplane is traveling at a rate of 180 miles per hour. The other airplane is traveling at a rate of 320 miles per hour. If the two planes are traveling in opposite directions, how long will it take for them to be 250 miles apart?

    A. 50 minutes   **B.** 1 hour   **C.** 45 minutes   **D.** $\dfrac{1}{2}$ hour   **18.** _____

19. If $A = \begin{bmatrix} -1 & -2 & 6 & 4 \\ 5 & 3 & 0 & 7 \end{bmatrix}$ and $B = \begin{bmatrix} 9 & 2 & -5 & 1 \\ -4 & 0 & 3 & -1 \end{bmatrix}$, find $2A + B$.

    A. $\begin{bmatrix} 10 & 2 & 3 & 7 \\ 3 & 5 & 5 & 8 \end{bmatrix}$ **B.** $\begin{bmatrix} 7 & 0 & 1 & 5 \\ 1 & 3 & 3 & 6 \end{bmatrix}$

    C. $\begin{bmatrix} 7 & -2 & 7 & 9 \\ 6 & 6 & 3 & 13 \end{bmatrix}$ **D.** $\begin{bmatrix} 16 & 0 & 2 & 10 \\ 2 & 6 & 6 & 12 \end{bmatrix}$ **19.** _____

20. A card is randomly drawn from a standard deck of 52 cards. What is the probability that it is a 5 or a diamond?

    A. $\dfrac{17}{52}$ **B.** $\dfrac{1}{52}$ **C.** $\dfrac{4}{13}$ **D.** $\dfrac{1}{4}$ **20.** _____

Glencoe Algebra 1

Second Semester Test (continued)
(Chapters 7–14)

For Questions 21–23, determine the best method to solve the system of equations. Then solve the system.

21. $7m + 12n = 31$
$20m - 12n = -4$

22. $5x + 6y = 9$
$y = 4x + 16$

23. $3x + 5y = 7$
$4x - 3y = -10$

24. Solve the system of inequalities by graphing.
$-2x + y < 1$
$x - 3y \leq 7$

21. _____

22. _____

23. _____

24.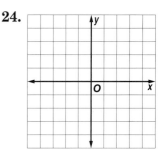

25. Simplify $\dfrac{(-4r^2s^{-5})^{-2}}{(2r^{-3})^{-2}}$.

25. _____

26. Evaluate $(2.4 \times 10^{-3})(1.9 \times 10^2)$. Express your answer in scientific and standard notation.

26. _____

27. Find $(5x^2 - x + 2) + (x^2 - 4x - 7)$.

27. _____

28. The sides of a rectangle are two consecutive even integers. Write an algebraic expression to represent the area.

28. _____

29. Find $(2y - 7)(y + 3)$.

29. _____

For Questions 31 and 32, factor each polynomial.

30. $t^2 - 7t + 6$

31. $3x^3 + 3x^2 - 12x - 12$

30. _____

31. _____

For Questions 33 and 34, solve each equation.

32. $7x^2 - 37x + 10 = 0$

32. _____

33. $4x^2 - 12x + 9 = 25$

33. _____

34. Solve $5m^2 + 3m = 7$ by using the Quadratic Formula. Round to the nearest tenth.

34. _____

35. Graph $y = \left(\dfrac{1}{8}\right)^x$. State the y-intercept. Then use the graph to determine the approximate value of $\left(\dfrac{1}{8}\right)^{-1.3}$.

35. _____

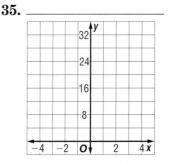

Second Semester Test (continued)
(Chapters 7–14)

36. Find the fifth term of a geometric sequence in which $a_1 = 3$ and $r = -4$.

36. _____

37. Solve $\sqrt{5x + 29} = x + 3$.

37. _____

38. Determine whether the side measures 9, 24, and 26 form a right triangle. Justify your answer.

38. _____

39. Find the possible values of a if the points $(a, 4)$ and $(20, 24)$ are 25 units apart.

39. _____

40. Find the missing measure x if $\triangle XWV \sim \triangle XYZ$.

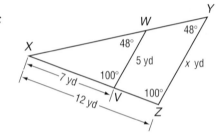

40. _____

41. Solve the right triangle ABC. State the side lengths to the nearest tenth and the angle measures to the nearest degree.

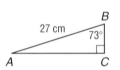

41. _____

42. Find $\dfrac{m - 3}{m + 4} \div \dfrac{m^2 - 4m + 3}{m^2 - 16}$.

42. _____

43. Find $(2x^2 + 3x - 5) \div (x - 3)$.

43. _____

44. Find $\dfrac{2y + 4}{y + 1} + \dfrac{3y}{4y + 4}$.

44. _____

45. Simplify $\dfrac{z - \dfrac{3}{z - 2}}{z - \dfrac{6}{z - 1}}$.

45. _____

46. Solve $\dfrac{15}{x^2 - 5x} + \dfrac{3}{5 - x} = 4$.

46. _____

47. The number of new productions on Broadway each season from 1985 to 2000 is listed below. Find the range, median, lower quartile, upper quartile, and interquartile range of the set of data. Identify any outliers.
34 41 30 33 40 28 37 34 39 33 38 37 33 39 37

47. _____

48. Mark bought seeds, 5 packets of carrot seeds, 2 packets of bean seeds, and 3 packets of pea seeds. If he randomly selects 4 packets to plant, what is the probability that he selects 2 packets of carrots, 1 packet of beans, and 1 packet of peas?

48. _____

Final Test
(Chapters 1–14)

1. Evaluate $10(4 + 3 \cdot 2) \div (2 \cdot 6 - 7)$.

   A. 4   **B.** 20   **C.** 28   **D.** 100   1. _____

2. Find the solution set for $5x - 8 \leq 5.5$ if the replacement set is {2.3, 2.5, 2.7, 2.9, 3.1}.

   A. {2.3, 2.5}   **B.** {2.7, 2.9, 3.1}   **C.** {2.3, 2.5, 2.7}   **D.** {2.7}   2. _____

3. Which numbers are counterexamples for the statement.
   If the sum of x and y is positive, then both x and y are positive.

   A. $x = 4, y = -2$ **B.** $x = 6, y = 5$

   C. $x = -3, y = -7$ **D.** $x = 1, y = -8$ 3. _____

4. Evaluate $\dfrac{x - 4y}{z - y}$ if $x = 8, y = -2.5$, and $z = 1.5$.

   A. 4.5   **B.** 17.2   **C.** 14.5   **D.** 5.3   4. _____

5. If $-\dfrac{73}{11}, \sqrt{44}, -6.\overline{64}, \dfrac{53}{8}$ were put in order from least to greatest, which would be the third number in the list?

   A. $-\dfrac{73}{11}$ **B.** $\sqrt{44}$ **C.** $-6.\overline{64}$ **D.** $\dfrac{53}{8}$ 5. _____

6. Solve $4(3 + 2x) - 8 = 8x + 4$.

   A. 0   **B.** 2   **C.** all numbers   **D.** no solution   6. _____

7. A pair of hiking boots is on sale for 35% off the original price. If the original price of the boots is $72, what is the discounted price?

   A. $25.20   **B.** $46.80   **C.** $97.20   **D.** $54.00   7. _____

8. Solve $6u + t = 4u + vw$ for u.

   A. $u = \dfrac{vw + t}{10}$ **B.** $u = \dfrac{4u + vw - t}{6}$ **C.** $t = vw - 2u$ **D.** $u = \dfrac{vw - t}{2}$ 8. _____

9. Solve $y = 3x + 7$ if the domain is $\{-4, -2, 0, 1, 3\}$.

   A. $\{(-5, -4), (1, -2), (7, 0), (10, 1), (16, 3)\}$
   B. $\{(-4, -12), (-2, -6), (0, 0), (1, 3), (3, 9)\}$
   C. $\{(-12, -4), (-6, -2), (0, 0), (3, 1), (9, 3)\}$
   D. $\{(-4, -5), (-2, 1), (0, 7), (1, 10), (3, 16)\}$ 9. _____

10. Which equation is represented by the graph?

    A. $4x + 5y = 20$ **B.** $5x - 4y = -20$

    C. $y = \dfrac{4}{5}x + 5$ **D.** $y = \dfrac{5}{4}x - 5$ 10. _____

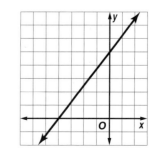

Final Test *(continued)*
(Chapters 1–14)

11. If $f(x) = x^2 - 3x$, find $f(-5)$.

   A. 40   **B.** 10   **C.** 25   **D.** -10 **11.** _____

12. If y varies directly as x and $y = 14$ when $x = 8$, find x when $y = 21$.

   A. $\dfrac{147}{4}$ **B.** $\dfrac{16}{3}$ **C.** 12   **D.** $\dfrac{1}{12}$ **12.** _____

13. Write the slope-intercept form of an equation for the line that passes through $(-4, -1)$ and is parallel to the graph of $6x - y = 6$.

   A. $y = 6x + 23$ **B.** $y = 6x - 23$

   C. $y = -6x - 25$ **D.** $y = \dfrac{1}{6}x - \dfrac{1}{3}$ **13.** _____

14. Solve $2(2t + 4) - 5 \geq 4(t + 2) - 3$.

   A. $\{t \mid t \geq 3\}$ **B.** $\varnothing$ **C.** $\{t \mid t \leq 5\}$ **D.** $\{t \mid t \leq 0\}$ **14.** _____

15. Which graph represents the solution of $|2w + 5| \leq 3$?

   A.

   B.

   C.

   D.   **15.** _____

16. How many solutions exist for the system of equations $x + 6y = 12$ and $2x + 12y = 1$?

   A. no solution   **B.** one solution

   C. two solutions   **D.** infinitely many solutions   **16.** _____

17. If $4x - 5y = 4$ and $6x - 7y = 10$, what is the value of x?

   A. 8   **B.** -8 **C.** 11   **D.** -11 **17.** _____

18. Evaluate $(3.1 \times 10^{-2})(2.5 \times 10^2)$.

   A. 0   **B.** 775   **C.** 77.5   **D.** 7.75   **18.** _____

19. Arrange the terms of the polynomial $3x^4 - 2xy + 5y^3$ so that the powers of x are in ascending order.

   A. $5y^3 + 3x^4 - 2xy$ **B.** $3x^4 - 2xy + 5y^3$

   C. $5y^3 - 2xy + 3x^4$ **D.** $-2xy + 3x^4 + 5y^3$ **19.** _____

20. Find $(x^2 - 2x + 1)(x^2 + 3x - 4)$.

   A. $x^3 - 7x^2 + 11x - 4$ **B.** $x^4 + x^3 - 10x^2 + 8x$

   C. $x^4 + x^3 - 9x^2 + 11x - 4$ **D.** $x^4 + 5x^3 + 11x^2 + 11x + 4$ **20.** _____

21. Factor $3x^2 - 12x + 12$.

   A. $(3x - 4)(x - 3)$ **B.** $3(x - 2)^2$

   C. $3(x - 2)(x + 2)$ **D.** $(3x - 6)(x - 2)$ **21.** _____

Final Test (continued)
(Chapters 1–14)

22. Solve $5x^2 - 9x - 8 = 9x$.

A. $\left\{-\frac{2}{5}, 4\right\}$ **B.** $\pm\frac{2\sqrt{10}}{5}$ **C.** $\left\{-\frac{4}{5}, 2\right\}$ **D.** $\left\{-2, \frac{4}{5}\right\}$ 22. _____

23. Solve $g^2 - 6g + 9 = 49$.

A. $\{3, 7\}$ **B.** $\{-10, 4\}$ **C.** $\{-4, 10\}$ **D.** $\{-3, -7\}$ 23. _____

24. State the value of the discriminant for $6y^2 + 9y + 2 = 0$.

A. 33   **B.** −5.7   **C.** 69   **D.** −36   24. _____

25. Find the geometric mean in the sequence 6, __?__, 96.

A. ±24   **B.** 4   **C.** ±16   **D.** 51   25. _____

26. Solve $2 + \sqrt{3x - 6} = x$.

A. $\{2, 4\}$ **B.** $\{2, 5\}$ **C.** $\{3, 5\}$ **D.** $\{3, 4\}$ 26. _____

27. First street and Broadway Avenue form a right angle. The distance between Broadway Avenue and Main Street is one mile. The distance between First Street and Third Street is two miles. What is the distance along the train tracks from the intersection of Main Street and First Street to the intersection of Broadway Avenue and Third Street?

Main Street

First Street

1 mile

2 miles

Broadway Avenue

Third Street

A. 2.2 miles   **B.** 3 miles   **C.** 2.5 miles   **D.** 1.5 miles   27. _____

28. Find $\dfrac{t^2 + 4t - 21}{t^2 - t - 6} \cdot \dfrac{4t + 8}{3t + 21}$.

A. $\dfrac{t - 7}{t + 7}$ **B.** $\dfrac{(t - 7)(t + 3)}{(t - 3)(t + 7)}$ **C.** 1   **D.** $\dfrac{4}{3}$ 28. _____

29. Solve $\dfrac{3}{x - 4} + \dfrac{x}{x + 4} = 1$.

A. −28   **B.** 28   **C.** $-\dfrac{4}{7}$ **D.** $\dfrac{4}{7}$ 29. _____

30. Carlos has 3 quarters, 5 dimes, and 4 nickels in his pocket. If he randomly selects 2 coins for a toll, what is the probability that the coins are 1 quarter and 1 nickel?

A. $\dfrac{1}{12}$ **B.** $\dfrac{1}{11}$ **C.** $\dfrac{7}{12}$ **D.** $\dfrac{27}{44}$ 30. _____

31. Evaluate $16 \div 2 \cdot 4 - 5 \cdot 1$.

A. −8   **B.** −160   **C.** 27   **D.** −3   31. _____

Assessment

Final Test *(continued)*
(Chapters 1–14)

32. Simplify $3(m + 4n) + 2(5m + 3n) + 7m$.

32. _____

33. Identify the hypothesis and conclusion of the statement. Then write the statement in if-then form. *I only go to Hawaii when I am on vacation.*

33. _____

34. Evaluate $\dfrac{\left|x + \frac{1}{3}\right| - |y|}{\frac{2}{3} - 2z}$ if $x = \dfrac{1}{2}$, $y = -\dfrac{1}{6}$, and $z = \dfrac{1}{6}$.

34. _____

35. A computer randomly picks a two-digit number greater than 49. Find the odds that the number picked is a multiple of 5.

35. _____

36. Name the set or sets of numbers to which the real number $\sqrt{44}$ belongs.

36. _____

37. Translate the following sentence into an algebraic equation. *Fifteen less a number t is four more than the sum of seven and t divided by two.*

37. _____

38. Solve $6(x + 1) - 4 = 3x + 2$. Then check your solution.

38. _____

39. Find the total price of a phone that costs $85.00 if the sales tax rate is 4%.

39. _____

40. A 5-pound can contains two different kinds of nuts, and costs $16. One type of nut costs $3.50 a pound. The other type costs $2.75 a pound. How many pounds of the less expensive type of nut are in the can?

40. _____

41. Find the coordinates of the vertices of parallelogram $QRST$ with $Q(-1, 1)$, $R(-3, 1)$, $S(-4, 3)$, and $T(-2, 3)$ reflected over the y-axis. Then graph the preimage and its image.

41. _____

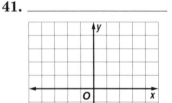

42. Express the relation shown in the mapping as a set of ordered pairs. Then write the inverse of the relation.

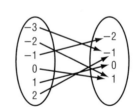

42. _____

43. Determine the x-intercept and y-intercept of $4x + 2y = -8$.

43. _____

44. Find the slope of the line that passes through $(5, -6)$ and $(3, -6)$.

44. _____

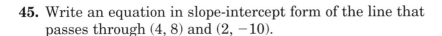

Final Test (continued)
(Chapters 1–14)

45. Write an equation in slope-intercept form of the line that passes through $(4, 8)$ and $(2, -10)$.

45. _____

46. Write the slope-intercept form for an equation of a line that passes through $(4, 3)$ and is perpendicular to the graph of $3y - 4x = 1$.

46. _____

47. Solve $10b - 8(b + 1) < 4(b - 2) + 6$.

47. _____

48. Solve $3m < -6$ or $2m + 7 > 13$.

48. _____

49. To join the Radio City Rockettes precision dance troupe, a woman must be within 2.5 inches of 68 inches tall. What are the acceptable heights in inches of a member of the Radio City Rockettes?

49. _____

50. Graph $y \geq -\frac{1}{3}x - 1$.

50.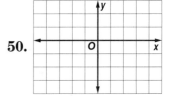

For Questions 51 and 52, solve each system of equations.

51. $x + y = 1$
    $y = 5x + 7$

51. _____

52. $4x + 3y = -1$
    $-3x - 2y = 3$

52. _____

53. The sum of the measures of two angles in a right triangle is $90°$, and the difference of their measures is $14°$. What are the measures of the two angles?

53. _____

54. A tax firm provides two services, a basic tax return and an in-depth return. The table gives the time requirements for each type of return.

54.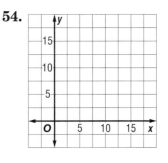

	Hours Per Basic Return	Hours Per In-Depth Return	Total Hours Available Each Week
Preparation	1	2	20
Review	1.2	1.2	20

Make a graph showing the number of each type of return that can be prepared and reviewed each week.

55. Simplify $\dfrac{(-2m^2n^{-4})^3}{(4m^{-5}n^3)^0}$.

55. _____

56. Solve $3x(2x + 5) - 12 = 6(x^2 - 1)$.

56. _____

57. Find $(3x - 2)(x^2 + x + 4)$.

57. _____

Final Test *(continued)*
(Chapters 1–14)

Factor each polynomial.

58. $4m^2 - 28mn + 49n^2$

59. $2x^3 + 4x^2 - 18x - 36$

For Questions 60 and 61, solve each equation.

60. $7x^2 - 30x = -8$

61. $3x^3 - 48x = 0$

62. Write the equation of the axis of symmetry, and find the coordinates of the vertex of the graph of $y = -x^2 - 2x - 4$.

63. Solve $0 = -2x^2 - 8x + 9$ by using the Quadratic Formula. Round solutions to the nearest tenth.

64. Determine whether the data in the table display exponential behavior. Explain why or why not.

x	−3	−1	1	3
y	6	12	24	48

65. Find the eighth term of a geometric sequence in which $a_1 = -7$ and $r = -2$.

66. Simplify $\dfrac{\sqrt{25a^3b^2}}{\sqrt{45a^2b^4}}$.

67. Solve $\sqrt{6y} + 5 = 17$.

68. A 10-ft ladder leans against the side of a house. The top of the ladder rests 8 ft above the ground. How far from the house is the base of the ladder?

69. Walter measured the angle of elevation to the top of a building to be 60°. Walter was 120 feet away from the base of the building when he calculated the angle of elevation. How tall is the building to the nearest foot?

70. Write an inverse variation equation that relates x and y if $y = 8$ when $x = -8$. Then find y when $x = 1.6$.

71. Simplify $\dfrac{m^2 - 1}{m^2 - m - 2}$. State the excluded values of the variable.

72. Find $(x^3 - 13x + 12) \div (x - 3)$.

73. Find $5\begin{bmatrix} -10 & 5 & 0 \\ 2 & -7 & 16 \end{bmatrix} - \begin{bmatrix} -6 & 17 & -2 \\ 5 & 12 & 19 \end{bmatrix}$.

58. _____

59. _____

60. _____

61. _____

62. _____

63. _____

64. _____

65. _____

66. _____

67. _____

68. _____

69. _____

70. _____

71. _____

72. _____

73. _____

Glencoe Algebra 1

14 # Standardized Test Practice

Student Record Sheet *(Use with pages 794–795 of the Student Edition.)*

Part 1 Multiple Choice

Select the best answer from the choices given and fill in the corresponding oval.

1 Ⓐ Ⓑ Ⓒ Ⓓ   4 Ⓐ Ⓑ Ⓒ Ⓓ   7 Ⓐ Ⓑ Ⓒ Ⓓ

2 Ⓐ Ⓑ Ⓒ Ⓓ   5 Ⓐ Ⓑ Ⓒ Ⓓ   8 Ⓐ Ⓑ Ⓒ Ⓓ

3 Ⓐ Ⓑ Ⓒ Ⓓ   6 Ⓐ Ⓑ Ⓒ Ⓓ   9 Ⓐ Ⓑ Ⓒ Ⓓ

Part 2 Short Response/Grid In

Solve the problem and write your answer in the blank.

For Questions 13 and 14, also enter your answer by writing each number or symbol in a box. Then fill in the corresponding oval for that number or symbol.

10 _____

11 _____

12 _____

13 _____ (grid in)

14 _____ (grid in)

13

14

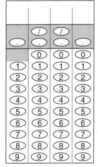

Part 3 Quantitative Comparison

Select the best answer from the choices given and fill in the corresponding oval.

15 Ⓐ Ⓑ Ⓒ Ⓓ

16 Ⓐ Ⓑ Ⓒ Ⓓ

17 Ⓐ Ⓑ Ⓒ Ⓓ

Part 4 Open-Ended

Record your answers for Question 18 on the back of this paper.

NAME _____ DATE _____ PERIOD _____

14-1 Study Guide and Intervention

Counting Outcomes

Tree Diagrams One method used for counting the number of possible outcomes of an event is to draw a **tree diagram**. The last column of the tree diagram shows all of the possible outcomes. The list of all possible outcomes is called the **sample space**, and a specific outcome is called an **event**.

Example 1 Suppose you can set up a stereo system with a choice of video, DVD, or laser disk players, a choice of cassette or graphic equalizer audio components, and a choice of single or dual speakers. Draw a tree diagram to show the sample space.

Player	Audio	Speaker	Outcomes
video	cassette	Single	VCS
		Dual	VCD
	graphic equalizer	Single	VGS
		Dual	VGD
DVD	cassette	Single	DCS
		Dual	DCD
	graphic equalizer	Single	DGS
		Dual	DGD
laser disk	cassette	Single	LCS
		Dual	LCD
	graphic equalizer	Single	LGS
		Dual	LGD

The tree diagram shows that there are 12 ways to set up the stereo system.

Example 2 A food stand offers ice cream cones in vanilla or chocolate flavors. It also offers fudge or caramel toppings, and it uses sugar or cake cones. Use a tree diagram to determine the number of possible ice cream cones.

Flavor	Toppings	Cone	Outcomes
vanilla	fudge	sugar	VFS
		cake	VFC
	caramel	sugar	VCS
		cake	VCC
chocolate	fudge	sugar	CFS
		cake	CFC
	caramel	sugar	CCS
		cake	CCC

The tree diagram shows that there are 8 possible ice cream cones.

Exercises

The spinner at the right is spun twice.

1. Draw a tree diagram to show the sample space.

A	B	C	D
A B C D	A B C D	A B C D	A B C D
AA AB AC AD	BA BB BC BD	CA CB CC CD	DA DB DC DD

2. How many outcomes are possible? **16**

A pizza can be ordered with a choice of sausage, pepperoni, or mushrooms for toppings, a choice of thin or pan for the crust, and a choice of medium or large for the size.

Toppings	Crust	Size	Outcomes
sausage	thin	medium	STM
		large	STL
	pan	medium	SPM
		large	SPL
pepperoni	thin	medium	PTM
		large	PTL
	pan	medium	PPM
		large	PPL
mushrooms	thin	medium	MTM
		large	MTL
	pan	medium	MPM
		large	MPL

3. Draw a tree diagram to show the sample space.

4. How many pizzas are possible? **12**

NAME _____ DATE _____ PERIOD _____

14-1 Study Guide and Intervention *(continued)*

Counting Outcomes

The Fundamental Counting Principle Another way to count the number of possible outcomes is to use the Fundamental Counting Principle.

Fundamental Counting Principle	If an event M can occur in m ways and an event N can occur in n ways, then M followed by N can occur in m · n ways.

Example Carly and Jake went to an arcade with 9 different games.

a. In how many different orders can they play the games if they play each one only once?

The number of orders for playing can be found by multiplying the number of choices for each position. Let *n* represent the number of possible orders.

$n = 9 \cdot 8 \cdot 7 \cdot 6 \cdot 5 \cdot 4 \cdot 3 \cdot 2 \cdot 1 = 362,880$

There are 362,880 ways to play each of 9 arcade games once. This is also known as a **factorial**, or $n = 9! = 9 \cdot 8 \cdot 7 \cdot 6 \cdot 5 \cdot 4 \cdot 3 \cdot 2 \cdot 1$.

b. If they have only enough tokens to play 6 different games, how many ways can they do this?

Use the Fundamental Counting Principle to find the sample space. There are 9 choices for the first game, 8 choices for the second, and so on, down to 4 choices for the sixth game.

$n = 9 \cdot 8 \cdot 7 \cdot 6 \cdot 5 \cdot 4 = 60,480$

There are 60,480 ways to play 6 different arcade games once.

Exercises

Find the value of each expression.

1. 6! **720**

2. 11! **39,916,800**

3. 8! **40,320**

4. A sub sandwich restaurant offers four types of sub sandwiches, three different types of potato chips, five types of bread, and six different beverages. How many different sandwich and drink combinations can you order? **360**

5. How many outfits are possible if you can choose one from each of four shirts, three pairs of pants, two pairs of shoes, and two jackets? **48**

6. In how many ways can you arrange 5 boxes of cereal on a shelf? **120**

7. Seven students sit in a row in the auditorium. In how many ways can they arrange themselves? **5,040**

8. Kinjal puts 12 different books on a shelf. In how many different ways can she arrange them? **479,001,600**

NAME _____ DATE _____ PERIOD _____

14-1 Skills Practice
Counting Outcomes

Draw a tree diagram to show the sample space for each event. Determine the number of possible outcomes.

1. planting a garden with roses, zinnias, or cosmos, in yellow, red, orange, or purple

Flower	Color	Outcomes
roses	yellow	RY
	red	RR
	orange	RO
	purple	RP
zinnias	yellow	ZY
	red	ZR
	orange	ZO
	purple	ZP
cosmos	yellow	CY
	red	CR
	orange	CO
	purple	CP

There are 12 possible outcomes.

2. selecting monogrammed or plain stationery, in white or buff, with lined or unlined envelopes

Stationery	Color	Envelope	Outcomes
monogrammed	white	lined	MWL
		unlined	MWU
	buff	lined	MBL
		unlined	MBU
plain	white	lined	PWL
		unlined	PWU
	buff	lined	PBL
		unlined	PBU

There are 8 possible outcomes.

Find the value of each expression.

3. 1! **1**   4. 3! **6**   5. 6! **720**   6. 9! **362,880**

7. Two dice are rolled. How many outcomes are possible? **36**

8. If students can choose between 7 elective subjects, 6 class periods, and 5 teachers, how many elective classes are possible? **210**

9. How many different ways can a carpenter build a bookcase using one each of 4 types of wood, 3 stains, 5 widths, and 6 heights? **360**

Lesson 14-1

NAME _____ DATE _____ PERIOD _____

14-1 Practice (Average)
Counting Outcomes

Draw a tree diagram to show the sample space for each event. Determine the number of possible outcomes.

1. dining at an Italian, Mexican, or French restaurant, for lunch, early bird (early dinner special), or dinner, and with or without dessert **18**

Style	Time	Dessert	Outcomes
Italian	lunch	dessert	ILD
		no dessert	ILN
	early bird	dessert	IED
		no dessert	IEN
	dinner	dessert	IDD
		no dessert	IDN
Mexican	lunch	dessert	MLD
		no dessert	MLN
	early bird	dessert	MED
		no dessert	MEN
	dinner	dessert	MDD
		no dessert	MDN
French	lunch	dessert	FLD
		no dessert	FLN
	early bird	dessert	FED
		no dessert	FEN
	dinner	dessert	FDD
		no dessert	FDN

There are 18 possible outcomes.

Find the value of each expression.

2. 5! **120**   3. 8! **40,320**   4. 10! **3,628,800**   5. 12! **479,001,600**

6. How many different vacation plans are possible when choosing one each of 12 destinations, 3 lengths of stay, 5 travel options, and 4 types of accommodations? **720**

7. How many different ways can you arrange your work if you can choose from 7 weekly schedules, 6 daily schedules, and one of 3 types of duties? **126**

8. How many different ways can you treat a minor cut if you can choose from 3 methods of cleansing the cut, 5 antibiotic creams, 2 antibacterial sprays, and 6 types of bandages? **180**

9. **TESTING** A teacher gives a quick quiz that has 4 true/false questions and 2 multiple choice questions, each of which has 5 answer choices. In how many ways can the quiz be answered if one answer is given for each question? **400**

CLASS RINGS Students at Pacific High can choose class rings in one each of 8 styles, 5 metals, 2 finishes, 14 stones, 7 cuts of stone, 4 tops, 3 printing styles, and 30 inscriptions.

10. How many different choices are there for a class ring? **2,822,400**

11. If a student narrows the choice to 2 styles, 3 metals, 4 cuts of stone, and 5 inscriptions (and has already made the remaining decisions), how many different choices for a ring remain? **120**

Left page

14-1 **Reading to Learn Mathematics**

Counting Outcomes

Pre-Activity **How are possible win/loss football records counted?**

Read the introduction to Lesson 14-1 at the top of page 754 in your textbook. Then complete the diagram.

Game 1	Game 2	Game 3	Outcomes
win	win	win	win-win-win
		lose	win-win-lose
	lose	win	win-lose-win
		lose	win-lose-lose
lose	win	win	lose-win-win
		lose	lose-win-lose
	lose	win	lose-lose-win
		lose	lose-lose-lose

Reading the Lesson

Use the tree diagram above for Exercises 1–4.

1. What is the sample space?

win-win-win, win-win-lose, win-lose-win, win-lose-lose, lose-win-win, lose-win-lose, lose-lose-win, lose-lose-lose

2. Name two different outcomes.

Sample answer: win-win-lose, win-lose-win

3. Three different outcomes result in a win/loss record of 2-1. What are they?

win-win-lose, win-lose-win, lose-win-win

4. Use the Fundamental Counting Principle to complete the chart.

	Game 1	Game 2	Game 3	Number of Outcomes
Number of Choices	2 ·	2 ·	2 =	8

Helping You Remember

5. Suppose you are training the new disc jockey for a school radio station. He has chosen 10 selections to play from a new CD. How could you use factorials to explain to him the number of different ways the selections could be played?

Multiply the number of possible choices for each slot on the playlist. There are 10 choices for the first song, nine choices for the second song, and so on. So the selections can be played in
$10 \cdot 9 \cdot 8 \cdot 7 \cdot 6 \cdot 5 \cdot 4 \cdot 3 \cdot 2 \cdot 1 = 3,628,800$ **ways.**

835

Glencoe Algebra 1

Right page

14-1 **Enrichment**

Pascal's Triangle

Pascal's Triangle is a pattern of numbers used at many levels of mathematics. It is named for Blaise Pascal, a seventeenth-century French mathematician who discovered several applications of the pattern. However, records of the triangle have been traced as far back as twelfth-century China and Persia. In the year 1303, the Chinese mathematician Zhū-Shìjié wrote *The Precious Mirror of the Four Elements*, in which he described how the triangle could be used to solve polynomial equations. The figure at the right is adapted from the original Chinese manuscript. In the figure, some circles are empty while others contain Chinese symbols.

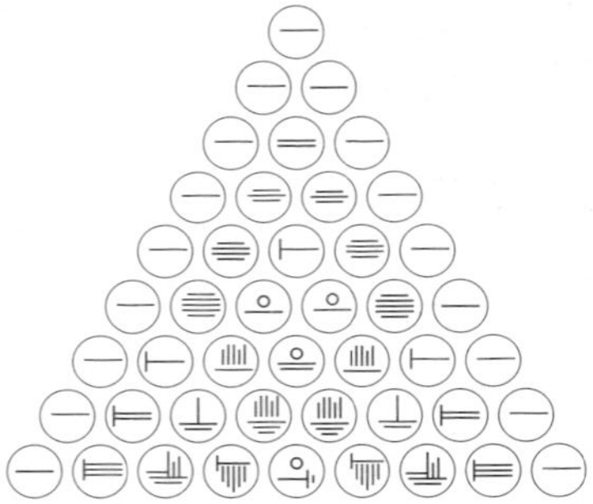

At the right, a portion of Pascal's Triangle is shown using Hindu-Arabic numerals.

The triangle expresses a relationship between numbers that you can discover by comparing the Chinese version and the Hindu-Arabic version.

1. What Chinese symbol corresponds to the Hindu-Arabic numeral 1?

2. Fill in the outermost circles in the Chinese version of Pascal's Triangle.

3. What Chinese symbol corresponds to the Hindu-Arabic numeral 4?

4. What Chinese symbol corresponds to the Hindu-Arabic numeral 10? ○

5. Based upon your investigation so far, fill in as many of the missing numbers as you can in both the Chinese and Hindu-Arabic versions of Pascal's Triangle.

6. Pascal's Triangle is *symmetric* about an imaginary vertical line that separates the left and right halves of the triangle. Use this fact to fill in more missing numbers in the triangles.

7. Each row of the triangle is generated from the row above by using a simple rule. Find the rule. Then fill in the remaining entries in both triangles.

Each entry is the sum of the two numbers at the left and right in row directly above.

836

Glencoe Algebra 1

NAME _____ DATE _____ PERIOD _____

14-2 Study Guide and Intervention

Permutations and Combinations

Permutations An arrangement or listing in which order or placement is important is called a **permutation**. For example the arrangement AB of choices A and B is different from the arrangement BA of these same two choices.

Permutations	$_nP_r = \dfrac{n!}{(n-r)!}$

Example 1 Find $_6P_2$.

$_nP_r = \dfrac{n!}{(n-r)!}$ Definition of $_nP_r$

$_6P_2 = \dfrac{6!}{(6-2)!}$ $n = 6, r = 2$

$= \dfrac{6!}{4!}$ Simplify.

$= \dfrac{6 \cdot 5 \cdot 4 \cdot 3 \cdot 2 \cdot 1}{4 \cdot 3 \cdot 2 \cdot 1}$ Definition of factorial

$= 6 \cdot 5$ or 30 Simplify.

There are 30 permutations of 6 objects taken 2 at a time.

Example 2 A specific program requires the user to enter a 5-digit password. The digits cannot repeat and can be any five of the digits 1, 2, 3, 4, 7, 8, and 9.

a. How many different passwords are possible?

$_nP_r = \dfrac{n!}{(n-r)!}$

$_7P_5 = \dfrac{7!}{(7-5)!}$

$= \dfrac{7 \cdot 6 \cdot 5 \cdot 4 \cdot 3 \cdot 2 \cdot 1}{2 \cdot 1}$

$= 7 \cdot 6 \cdot 5 \cdot 4 \cdot 3$ or 2520

There are 2520 ways to create a password.

b. What is the probability that the first two digits are odd numbers with the other digits any of the remaining numbers?

$P(\text{first two digits odd}) = \dfrac{\text{number of favorable outcomes}}{\text{number of possible outcomes}}$

Since there are 4 odd digits, the number of choices for the first digit is 4, and the number of choices for the second digit is 3. Then there are 5 choices left for the third digit, 4 for the fourth, and 3 for the fifth, so the number of favorable outcomes is $4 \cdot 3 \cdot 5 \cdot 4 \cdot 3$, or 720.

The probability is $\dfrac{720}{2520} \approx 28.6\%$.

Exercises

Evaluate of each expression.

1. $_7P_4$ **840** **2.** $_{12}P_7$ **3,991,680** **3.** $(_9P_4)(_{16}P_2)$ **87,091,200**

4. A club with ten members wants to choose a president, vice-president, secretary, and treasurer. Six of the members are women, and four are men.

a. How many different sets of officers are possible? **5040**

b. What is the probability that all officers will be women. **7.1%**

© Glencoe/McGraw-Hill 837 *Glencoe Algebra 1*

NAME _____ DATE _____ PERIOD _____

14-2 Study Guide and Intervention *(continued)*

Permutations and Combinations

Combinations An arrangement or listing in which order is not important is called a **combination**. For example, AB and BA are the same combination of A and B.

Combinations	$_nC_r = \dfrac{n!}{(n-r)!r!}$

Example A club with ten members wants to choose a committee of four members. Six of the members are women, and four are men.

a. How many different committees are possible?

$_nC_r = \dfrac{n!}{(n-r)!r!}$ Definition of combination

$= \dfrac{10!}{(10-4)!4!}$ $n = 10, r = 4$

$= \dfrac{10 \cdot 9 \cdot 8 \cdot 7}{4!}$ Divide by the GCF 6!.

$= 210$ Simplify.

There are 210 ways to choose a committee of four when order is not important.

b. If the committee is chosen randomly, what is the probability that two members of the committee are men?

There are $_4C_2 = \dfrac{4!}{(4-2)!2!} = 6$ ways to choose two men randomly, and there are $_6C_2 = \dfrac{6!}{(6-4)!4!} = 15$ ways to choose two women randomly. By the Fundamental Counting Principle, there are $6 \cdot 15 = 90$ ways to choose a committee with two men and two women.

Probability (2 men and 2 women) $= \dfrac{\text{number of favorable outcomes}}{\text{number of possible outcomes}}$

$= \dfrac{90}{210}$ or about 42.9%

Exercises

Find the value of each expression.

1. $_7C_3$ **35** **2.** $_{12}C_8$ **495** **3.** $(_9C_9)(_{11}C_9)$ **55**

4. In how many ways can a club with 9 members choose a two-member sub-committee? **36**

5. A book club offers its members a book each month for a year from a selection of 24 books. Ten of the books are biographies and 14 of the books are fiction.

a. How many ways could the members select 12 books? **2,704,156**

b. What is the probability that 5 biographies and 7 fiction books will be chosen? **about 32%**

© Glencoe/McGraw-Hill 838 *Glencoe Algebra 1*

Answers (Lesson 14-2)

14-2 Skills Practice
Permutations and Combinations

Determine whether each situation involves a *permutation* or *combination*. Explain your reasoning. Sample explanations are given.

1. dinner guests seated around a table **Permutation; The seating arrangement depends on the order in which guests are seated.**

2. a pattern of different widths of bars and spaces for a bar code **Permutation; The code depends on the order of the bars and spaces.**

3. selecting two yellow marbles out of a sack of yellow and blue marbles **Combination; The order in which the marbles are selected is not important.**

4. placing one can of each of 15 different types of soup along a store shelf **Permutation; The arrangement depends on the order in which the cans are placed.**

5. selecting four candles from a box of ten **Combination; The order does not matter in selecting the four candles.**

6. the placement of the top ten finishers in a school's spelling bee **Permutation; Placing the finishers means arranging them in order.**

7. choosing two colors of paint out of twenty to paint the walls and trim of a bedroom **Combination; The order in which the paints are chosen does not affect the selection.**

8. choosing a set of twelve pencils from a selection of thirty-six **Combination; The set of pencils is not based on any particular order or arrangement.**

Evaluate each expression.

9. $_5P_2$ **20**

10. $_6P_4$ **360**

11. $_7P_3$ **210**

12. $_9P_4$ **3024**

13. $_7P_5$ **2520**

14. $_5P_3$ **60**

15. $_6C_2$ **15**

16. $_9C_7$ **36**

17. $_8C_4$ **70**

18. $_7C_5$ **21**

19. $_{12}C_2$ **66**

20. $_{13}C_7$ **1716**

21. $_{11}C_2$ **55**

22. $_5P_4$ **120**

23. $_{14}C_5$ **2002**

24. $_{11}C_6$ **462**

25. $(_4P_2)(_3P_2)$ **72**

26. $(_8C_6)(_5P_1)$ **140**

839

14-2 Practice (Average)
Permutations and Combinations

Determine whether each situation involves a *permutation* or *combination*. Explain your reasoning. Sample explanations are given.

1. choosing two dogs from a litter of two males and three females **Combination; The order is not important in the choice of the two dogs.**

2. a simple melody formed by playing the notes on 8 different piano keys **Permutation; The sound of the melody depends on the order in which the notes are played.**

3. a selection of nine muffins from a shelf of twenty-three **Combination; The order does not matter in the selection of the muffins.**

4. the selection of a four-letter acronym (word formed from the initial letters of other words) in which two of the letters cannot be C or P **Permutation; The letters of the acronym must be arranged in a certain order.**

5. choosing an alphanumeric password to access a website **Permutation; The choice of letters and numbers must be in an exact order for the password to work.**

Evaluate each expression.

6. $_{11}P_3$ **990**

7. $_6P_3$ **120**

8. $_{15}P_3$ **2730**

9. $_{10}C_9$ **10**

10. $_{12}C_9$ **220**

11. $_7C_3$ **35**

12. $_7C_4$ **35**

13. $_{12}C_4$ **495**

14. $_{13}P_3$ **1716**

15. $(_8C_4)(_8C_5)$ **3920**

16. $(_{17}C_2)(_8C_6)$ **3808**

17. $(_{16}C_{15})(_{16}C_1)$ **256**

18. $(_8P_3)(_8P_2)$ **18,816**

19. $(_5P_4)(_6P_5)$ **86,400**

20. $(_{13}P_1)(_{15}P_1)$ **195**

21. $(_{10}C_3)(_{10}P_3)$ **86,400**

22. $(_{15}C_4)(_4C_3)$ **131,040**

23. $(_{14}C_7)(_{15}P_3)$ **9,369,360**

24. **SPORT** In how many orders can the top five finishers in a race finish? **120**

JUDICIAL PROCEDURE The court system in a community needs to assign 3 out of 8 judges to a docket of criminal cases. Five of the judges are male and three are female.

25. Does the selection of judges involve a permutation or a combination? **combination**

26. In how many ways could three judges be chosen? **56**

27. If the judges are chosen randomly, what is the probability that all 3 judges are male? $\frac{5}{28}$, **or about 18%**

840

Glencoe Algebra 1

14-2 Reading to Learn Mathematics

Permutations and Combinations

Pre-Activity **How can combinations be used to form committees?**

Read the introduction to Lesson 14-2 at the top of page 760 in your textbook.

What is meant by the term *combination?*

A group of objects not arranged in any particular order

Reading the Lesson

Complete the chart.

	Situation	Permutation or Combination?	Explain Your Choice
1.	3 of 7 students are chosen to go to a job fair	combination	See students' work.
2.	arrangement of student work for the school art show	permutation	See students' work.
3.	4-digit student I.D. numbers	permutation	See students' work.
4.	choosing 4 out of 12 possible pizza toppings	combination	See students' work.

Helping You Remember

5. To help you remember how the terms *permutation* and *combination* are different, think of everyday words that start with the letters P and C and that illustrate the meaning of each word. Explain how the words illustrate the two terms.

Sample answer: P for *phone number,* since the order of the digits in a phone number is important; C for *club,* since who is in a club is the important thing, not the order in which the names of the club members are listed

---

14-2 Enrichment

Latin Squares

In designing a statistical experiment, it is important to try to randomize the variables. For example, suppose 4 different motor oils are being compared to see which give the best gasoline mileage. An experimenter might then choose 4 different drivers and four different cars. To test-drive all the possible combinations, the experimenter would need 64 test-drives.

To reduce the number of test drives, a statistician might use an arrangement called a **Latin Square**.

For this example, the four motor oils are labeled A, B, C, and D and are arranged as shown. Each oil must appear exactly one time in each row and column of the square.

The drivers are labeled D_1, D_2, D_3, and D_4; the cars are labeled C_1, C_2, C_3, and C_4.

	D_1	D_2	D_3	D_4
C_1	A	B	C	D
C_2	B	A	D	C
C_3	C	D	A	B
C_4	D	C	B	A

Now, the number of test-drives is just 16, one for each cell of the Latin Square.

Create two 4-by-4 Latin Squares that are different from the example. **Answers will vary. Sample answers are given.**

1.

	D_1	D_2	D_3	D_4
C_1	B	C	A	D
C_2	D	A	C	B
C_3	C	D	B	A
C_4	A	B	D	C

2.

	D_1	D_2	D_3	D_4
C_1	D	C	B	A
C_2	A	B	C	D
C_3	B	D	A	C
C_4	C	A	D	B

Make three different 3-by-3 Latin Squares.

3.

	D_1	D_2	D_3
C_1	A	B	C
C_2	B	C	A
C_3	C	A	B

4.

	D_1	D_2	D_3
C_1	A	C	B
C_2	C	B	A
C_3	B	A	C

5.

	D_1	D_2	D_3
C_1	B	C	A
C_2	C	A	B
C_3	A	B	C

Answers

14-3 Study Guide and Intervention
Probability of Compound Events

Independent and Dependent Events Compound events are made up of two or more simple events. The events can be **independent events** or they can be **dependent events**.

Probability of Independent Events	Outcome of first event does not affect outcome of second.	$P(A \text{ and } B) = P(A) \cdot P(B)$	Example: rolling a 6 on a die and then rolling a 5
Probability of Dependent Events	Outcome of first event does affect outcome of second.	$P(A \text{ and } B) = P(A) \cdot P(B \text{ following } A)$	Example: without replacing the first card, choosing an ace and then a king from a deck of cards

Example 1 **Find the probability that you will roll a six and then a five when you roll a die twice.**

By the definition of independent events, $P(A \text{ and } B) = P(A) \cdot P(B)$.

First roll: $P(6) = \frac{1}{6}$

Second roll: $P(5) = \frac{1}{6}$

$P(6 \text{ and } 5) = P(6) \cdot P(5)$
$= \frac{1}{6} \cdot \frac{1}{6}$
$= \frac{1}{36}$

The probability that you will roll a six and then roll a five is $\frac{1}{36}$.

Example 2 **A bag contains 3 red marbles, 2 green marbles, and 4 blue marbles. Two marbles are drawn randomly from the bag and not replaced. Find the probability that both marbles are blue.**

By the definition of dependent events, $P(A \text{ and } B) = P(A) \cdot P(B \text{ following } A)$

First marble: $P(\text{blue}) = \frac{4}{9}$

Second marble: $P(\text{blue}) = \frac{3}{8}$

$P(\text{blue, blue}) = \frac{4}{9} \cdot \frac{3}{8}$
$= \frac{12}{72}$
$= \frac{1}{6}$

The probability of drawing two blue marbles is $\frac{1}{6}$.

Exercises

A bag contains 3 red, 4 blue, and 6 yellow marbles. One marble is selected at a time, and once a marble is selected, it is not replaced. Find each probability.

1. $P(2 \text{ yellow})$ $\dfrac{5}{26}$

2. $P(\text{red, yellow})$ $\dfrac{3}{26}$

3. $P(\text{blue, red, yellow})$ $\dfrac{6}{143}$

4. George has two red socks and two white socks in a drawer. What is the probability of picking a red sock and a white sock in that order if the first sock is not replaced? $\dfrac{1}{3}$

5. Phyllis drops a penny in a pond, and then she drops a nickel in the pond. What is the probability that both coins land with tails showing? $\dfrac{1}{4}$

6. A die is rolled and a penny is dropped. Find the probability of rolling a two and showing a tail. $\dfrac{1}{12}$

14-3 Study Guide and Intervention (continued)
Probability of Compound Events

Mutually Exclusive and Inclusive Events Events that cannot occur at the same time are called **mutually exclusive**. If two events are not mutually exclusive, they are called **inclusive**.

Probability of Mutually Exclusive Events	$P(A \text{ or } B) = P(A) + P(B)$	$P(\text{rolling a 2 or a 3 on a die}) = P(2) + P(3) = \frac{1}{3}$
Probability of Inclusive Events	$P(A \text{ or } B) = P(A) + P(B) - P(A \text{ and } B)$	$P(\text{King or Heart}) = P(K) + P(H) - P(K \text{ and } H) = \frac{9}{26}$

Example **Suppose a card is drawn from a standard deck of 52 cards. Find the probability of drawing a king or a queen.**

Drawing a king or a queen are mutually exclusive events.
By the definition of mutually exclusive events, $P(A \text{ or } B) = P(A) + P(B)$.

$P(A) = P(\text{king}) = \frac{4}{52} = \frac{1}{13}$ $\quad P(B) = P(\text{queen}) = \frac{4}{52} = \frac{1}{13}$

$P(\text{king or queen}) = \frac{1}{13} + \frac{1}{13}$
$= \frac{2}{13}$

The probability of drawing a king or a queen is $\frac{2}{13}$.

Exercises

A bag contains 2 red, 5 blue, and 7 yellow marbles. Find each probability.

1. $P(\text{yellow or red})$ $\dfrac{9}{14}$

2. $P(\text{red or not yellow})$ $\dfrac{1}{2}$

3. $P(\text{blue or red or yellow})$ 1

One card is drawn from a standard deck of 52 cards. Find each probability.

4. $P(\text{jack or red})$ $\dfrac{7}{13}$

5. $P(\text{red or black})$ 1

6. $P(\text{jack or clubs})$ $\dfrac{4}{13}$

7. $P(\text{queen or less than 3})$ $\dfrac{3}{13}$

8. $P(5 \text{ or } 6)$ $\dfrac{2}{13}$

9. $P(\text{diamond or spade})$ $\dfrac{1}{2}$

10. In a math class, 12 out of 15 girls are 14 years old and 14 out of 17 boys are 14 years old. What is the probability of selecting a girl or a 14-year old from this class? $\dfrac{29}{32}$

NAME _____ DATE _____ PERIOD _____

14-3 Skills Practice
Probability of Compound Events

A bag contains 2 green, 9 brown, 7 yellow, and 4 blue marbles. Once a marble is selected, it is not replaced. Find each probability.

1. P(brown, then yellow) $\frac{3}{22}$

2. P(green, then blue) $\frac{4}{231}$

3. P(yellow, then yellow) $\frac{1}{11}$

4. P(blue, then blue) $\frac{2}{77}$

5. P(green, then *not* blue) $\frac{17}{231}$

6. P(brown, then *not* green) $\frac{57}{154}$

A die is rolled and a spinner like the one at the right is spun. Find each probability.

7. P(4 and A) $\frac{1}{24}$

8. P(an even number and C) $\frac{1}{8}$

9. P(2 or 5 and B or D) $\frac{1}{6}$

10. P(a number less than 5 and B, C, or D) $\frac{1}{2}$

One card is drawn from a standard deck of 52 cards. Find each probability.

11. P(jack or ten) $\frac{2}{13}$

12. P(red or black) 1

13. P(queen or club) $\frac{4}{13}$

14. P(red or ace) $\frac{7}{13}$

15. P(diamond or black) $\frac{3}{4}$

16. P(face card or spade) $\frac{11}{26}$

Tiles numbered 1 through 20 are placed in a box. Tiles numbered 11 through 30 are placed in a second box. The first tile is randomly drawn from the first box. The second tile is randomly drawn from the second box. Find each probability.

17. P(both are greater than 15) $\frac{3}{16}$

18. The first tile is odd and the second tile is less than 25. $\frac{7}{20}$

19. The first tile is a multiple of 6 and the second tile is a multiple of 4. $\frac{3}{80}$

20. The first tile is less than 15 and the second tile is even or greater than 25. $\frac{21}{50}$

845

NAME _____ DATE _____ PERIOD _____

14-3 Practice (Average)
Probability of Compound Events

A bag contains 5 red, 3 brown, 6 yellow, and 2 blue marbles. Once a marble is selected, it is not replaced. Find each probability.

1. P(brown, then yellow, then red) $\frac{3}{112}$

2. P(red, then red, then blue) $\frac{1}{84}$

3. P(yellow, then yellow, then *not* blue) $\frac{3}{28}$

4. P(brown, then brown, then *not* yellow) $\frac{1}{70}$

A die is rolled and a card is drawn from a standard deck of 52 cards. Find each probability.

5. P(6 and king) $\frac{1}{78}$

6. P(odd number and black) $\frac{1}{4}$

7. P(less than 3 and heart) $\frac{1}{12}$

8. P(greater than 1 and black ace) $\frac{5}{156}$

One card is drawn from a standard deck of 52 cards. Find each probability.

9. P(spade or numbered card) $\frac{10}{13}$

10. P(ace or red queen) $\frac{3}{26}$

11. P(red or *not* face card) $\frac{23}{26}$

12. P(heart or *not* queen) $\frac{49}{52}$

Tiles numbered 1 through 25 are placed in a box. Tiles numbered 11 through 30 are placed in a second box. The first tile is randomly drawn from the first box. The second tile is randomly drawn from the second box. Find each probability.

13. P(both are greater than 15 and less than 20) $\frac{4}{125}$

14. The first tile is greater than 10 and the second tile is less than 25 or even. $\frac{51}{100}$

15. The first tile is a multiple of 3 or prime and the second tile is a multiple of 5. $\frac{16}{125}$

16. The first tile is less than 9 or odd and the second tile is a multiple of 4 or less than 21. $\frac{51}{125}$

17. **WEATHER** The forecast predicts a 40% chance of rain on Tuesday and a 60% chance on Wednesday. If these probabilities are independent, what is the chance that it will rain on both days? **24%**

FOOD Tomaso places favorite recipes in a bag for 4 pasta dishes, 5 casseroles, 3 types of chili, and 8 desserts.

18. If Tomaso chooses one recipe at random, what is the probability that he selects a pasta dish or a casserole? $\frac{9}{20}$

19. If Tomaso chooses one recipe at random, what is the probability that he does *not* select a dessert? $\frac{3}{5}$

20. If Tomaso chooses two recipes at random without replacement, what is the probability that the first recipe he selects is a casserole and the second recipe he selects is a dessert? $\frac{2}{19}$

846

Lesson 14-3

Answers (Lesson 14-3)

14-3 Reading to Learn Mathematics

Probability of Compound Events

Pre-Activity How are probabilities used by meteorologists?

Read the introduction to Lesson 14-3 at the top of page 769 in your textbook.

Is it more likely to rain or not rain on Saturday? on Sunday? Explain.

It is more likely not to rain on Saturday because the probability of rain is less than 50%; the reverse is true for Sunday.

Reading the Lesson

1. Complete the chart.

Term	Example	Formula
independent events	Rolling two dice	$P(A \text{ and } B) = P(A) \cdot P(B)$
dependent events	**Sample answer: Randomly choosing names from a hat without replacement**	$P(A \text{ and } B) = P(A) \cdot P(B \text{ following } A)$
mutually exclusive events	**Sample answer: Getting a number less than 3 and getting a number greater than 4 when rolling a die**	$P(A \text{ or } B) = P(A) + P(B)$
inclusive events	**Sample answer: Being born on Friday or on the 13th day of the month**	$P(A \text{ or } B) = P(A) + P(B) - P(A \text{ and } B)$

2. In probability, what is meant by the phrase *with replacement?*
After an item is chosen randomly, it is put back in and can be chosen again.

Helping You Remember

3. Look up the following terms in a dictionary. Write the definitions that best relate to the way these terms are used in probability. **See students' work.**

independent _____

dependent _____

exclusive _____

inclusive _____

Lesson 14-3

14-3 Enrichment

Conditional Probability

The probability of an event given the occurrence of another event is called **conditional probability**. The conditional probability of event A given event B is denoted $P(A|B)$.

Example Suppose a pair of number cubes is rolled. It is known that the sum is greater than seven. Find the probability that the number cubes match.

There are 15 sums greater than seven and there are 36 possible pairs altogether.

$$P(B) = \frac{15}{36}$$

There are three matching pairs greater than seven, (4, 4), (5, 5), and (6, 6).

$$P(A \text{ and } B) = \frac{3}{36}$$

$$P(A|B) = \frac{P(A \text{ and } B)}{P(B)}$$
$$= \frac{\frac{3}{36}}{\frac{15}{36}} \text{ or } \frac{1}{5}$$

The conditional probability is $\frac{1}{5}$.

A card is drawn from a standard deck of 52 cards and is found to be red. Given that event, find each of the following probabilities.

1. $P(\text{heart})$ $\frac{1}{2}$

2. $P(\text{ace})$ $\frac{1}{13}$

3. $P(\text{face card})$ $\frac{3}{13}$

4. $P(\text{jack or ten})$ $\frac{2}{13}$

5. $P(\text{six of spades})$ 0

6. $P(\text{six of hearts})$ $\frac{1}{26}$

A sports survey taken at Stirers High School shows that 48% of the respondents liked soccer, 66% liked basketball, and 38% liked hockey. Also, 30% liked soccer and basketball, 22% liked basketball and hockey, and 28% liked soccer and hockey. Finally, 12% liked all three sports.

7. Find the probability that Meg likes soccer if she likes basketball. $\frac{5}{11}$

8. Find the probability that Juan likes basketball if he likes soccer. $\frac{5}{8}$

9. Find the probability that Mieko likes hockey if she likes basketball. $\frac{1}{3}$

10. Find the probability that Greg likes hockey if he likes soccer. $\frac{7}{12}$

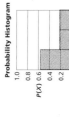

NAME _____ DATE _____ PERIOD _____

14-4 Study Guide and Intervention

Probability Distributions

Random Variables and Probability Distributions A random variable X is a variable whose value is the numerical outcome of a random event.

Example A teacher asked her students how many siblings they have. The results are shown in the table at the right.

Number of Siblings	Number of Students
0	1
1	15
2	8
3	2
4	1

a. Find the probability that a randomly selected student has 2 siblings.

The random variable X can equal 0, 1, 2, 3, or 4. In the table, the value $X = 2$ is paired with 8 outcomes, and there are 27 students surveyed.

$P(X = 2) = \dfrac{2\ \text{siblings}}{27\ \text{students surveyed}}$

$= \dfrac{8}{27}$

The probability that a randomly selected student has 2 siblings is $\dfrac{8}{27}$, or 29.6%.

b. Find the probability that a randomly selected student has at least three siblings.

$P(X \geq 3) = \dfrac{2 + 1}{27}$

The probability that a randomly selected student has at least 3 siblings is $\dfrac{1}{9}$, or 11.1%.

Exercises

For Exercises 1–3, use the grade distribution shown at the right. A grade of A = 5, B = 4, C = 3, D = 2, F = 1.

X = Grade	5	4	3	2	1
Number of Students	6	9	5	4	1

1. Find the probability that a randomly selected student in this class received a grade of C. **$\dfrac{1}{5}$**

2. Find the probability that a randomly selected student in this class received a grade lower than a C. **$\dfrac{1}{5}$**

3. What is the probability that a randomly selected student in this class passes the course, that is, gets at least a D? **$\dfrac{24}{25}$**

4. The table shows the results of tossing 3 coins 50 times. What is the probability of getting 2 or 3 heads? **48%**

X = Number of Heads	0	1	2	3
Number of Times	6	20	19	5

NAME _____ DATE _____ PERIOD _____

14-4 Study Guide and Intervention (continued)

Probability Distributions

Probability Distributions The probabilities associated with every possible value of the random variable X make up what are called the **probability distribution** for that variable. A probability distribution has the following properties.

Properties of a Probability Distribution	1. The probability of each value of X is greater than or equal to 0.
	2. The probabilities for all values of X add up to 1.

The probability distribution for a random variable can be given in a table or in a **probability histogram** and used to obtain other information.

Example The data from the example on page 849 can be used to determine a probability distribution and to make a probability histogram.

X = Number of Siblings	P(X)
0	0.037
1	0.556
2	0.296
3	0.074
4	0.037

Probability Histogram (0.600, 0.400, 0.200; X = Number of Siblings 0 1 2 3 4)

a. Show that the probability distribution is valid.

For each value of X, the probability is greater than or equal to 0 and less than or equal to 1. Also, the sum of the probabilities is 1.

b. What is the probability that a student chosen at random has fewer than 2 siblings?

Because the events are independent, the probability of fewer than 2 siblings is the sum of the probability of 0 siblings and the probability of 1 sibling, or $0.037 + 0.556 = 0.593$.

Exercises

The table at the right shows the probability distribution for students by school enrollment in the United States in 1997. Use the table for Exercises 1–3.

X = Type of School	P(X)
Elementary = 1	0.562
Secondary = 2	0.219
Higher Education = 3	0.219

Source: The New York Times Almanac.

1. Show that the probability distribution is valid.
$0 \leq P(X) \leq 1$; **the sum of the probabilities = 1**

2. If a student is chosen at random, what is the probability that the student is in elementary or secondary school? **0.781**

3. Make a probability histogram of the data.

Probability Histogram (1.0, 0.8, P(X) 0.6, 0.4, 0.2; X = Type of School 1 2 3)

Skills Practice (left page)

NAME _____ DATE _____ PERIOD _____

14-4 **Skills Practice**

Probability Distributions

For Exercises 1–3, the spinner shown is spun three times.

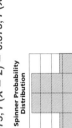

1. Write the sample space with all possible outcomes.
GGG, GGB, GBG, GBB, BGG, BGB, BBG, BBB

2. Find the probability distribution X, where X represents the number of times the spinner lands on green for $X = 0$, $X = 1$, $X = 2$, and $X = 3$.
$P(X = 0) = 0.125$, $P(X = 1) = 0.375$, $P(X = 2) = 0.375$, $P(X = 3) = 0.125$

3. Make a probability histogram.

Spinner Probability Distribution

For Exercises 4–7, the spinner shown is spun two times.

4. Write the sample space with all possible outcomes. RR, RB, RG, RY, BR, BB, BG, BY, GR, GB, GG, GY, YR, YB, YG, YY

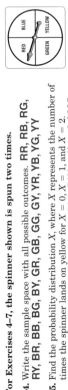

5. Find the probability distribution X, where X represents the number of times the spinner lands on yellow for $X = 0$, $X = 1$, and $X = 2$.
$P(X = 0) = 0.5625$, $P(X = 1) = 0.375$, $P(X = 2) = 0.0625$

6. Make a probability histogram.

Spinner Probability Distribution

BUSINESS For Exercises 7–9, use the table that shows the probability distribution of the number of minutes a customer spends at the express checkout at a supermarket.

X = Minutes	1	2	3	4	5+
Probability	0.09	0.13	0.28	0.32	0.18

7. Show that this is a valid probability distribution.
$0.09 + 0.13 + 0.28 + 0.32 + 0.18 = 1$

8. What is the probability that a customer spends less than 3 minutes at the checkout? **0.22**

9. What is the probability that the customer spends at least 4 minutes at the checkout? **0.50**

© Glencoe/McGraw-Hill   851   *Glencoe Algebra 1*

Practice (right page)

NAME _____ DATE _____ PERIOD _____

14-4 **Practice** (Average)

Probability Distributions

For Exercises 1–3, the spinner shown is spun two times.

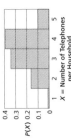

1. Write the sample space with all possible outcomes.
BB, BW, BR, BY, BG, WB, WW, WR, WY, WG, RB, RW, RR, RY, RG, YB, YW, YR, YY, YG, GB, GW, GR, GY, GG

2. Find the probability distribution X, where X represents the number of times the spinner lands on blue for $X = 0$, $X = 1$, and $X = 2$.
$P(X = 0) = 0.64$, $P(X = 1) = 0.32$, $P(X = 2) = 0.04$

3. Make a probability histogram.

Spinner Probability Distribution

TELECOMMUNICATIONS For Exercises 4–6, use the table that shows the probability distribution of the number of telephones per student's household at Wilson High.

X = Number of Telephones	1	2	3	4	5+
Probability	0.01	0.16	0.34	0.39	0.10

4. Show that this is a valid probability distribution.
$0.01 + 0.16 + 0.34 + 0.39 + 0.10 = 1$

5. If a student is chosen at random, what is the probability that there are more than 3 telephones at the student's home? **0.49**

6. Make a probability histogram.

Wilson High Households

LANDSCAPING For Exercises 7–9, use the table that shows the probability distribution of the number of shrubs (rounded to the nearest 50) ordered by corporate clients of a landscaping company over the past five years.

Number of Shrubs	50	100	150	200	250
Probability	0.11	0.24	0.45	0.16	0.04

7. Define a random variable and list its values. **Let X = the number of shrubs ordered; X = 50, 100, 150, 200, 250**

8. Show that this is a valid probability distribution.
$0.11 + 0.24 + 0.45 + 0.16 + 0.04 = 1$

9. What is the probability that a client's (rounded) order was at least 150 shrubs? **0.65**

© Glencoe/McGraw-Hill   852   *Glencoe Algebra 1*

NAME _____ DATE _____ PERIOD _____

14-4 Enrichment

Golden Rectangles

A **golden rectangle** has the property that its sides satisfy the following proportion.

$$\frac{a+b}{a} = \frac{a}{b}$$

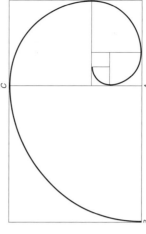
a

Two quadratic equations can be written from the proportion. These are sometimes called **golden quadratic** equations.

1. In the proportion, let $a = 1$. Use cross-multiplication to write a quadratic equation.
$b^2 + b - 1 = 0$

2. Solve the equation in Exercise 1 for b.
$b = \dfrac{-1 + \sqrt{5}}{2}$

3. In the proportion, let $b = 1$. Write a quadratic equation in a.
$a^2 - a - 1 = 0$

4. Solve the equation in Exercise 3 for a.
$a = \dfrac{1 + \sqrt{5}}{2}$

5. Explain why $\frac{1}{2}(\sqrt{5} + 1)$ and $\frac{1}{2}(\sqrt{5} - 1)$ are called golden ratios.
They are the ratios of the sides in a golden rectangle. The first is the ratio of the long side to the short side; the second is short side: long side.

Another property of golden rectangles is that a square drawn inside a golden rectangle creates another, smaller golden rectangle.

In the design at the right, opposite vertices of each square have been connected with quarters of circles.

For example, the arc from point B to point C is created by putting the point of a compass at point A. The radius of the arc is the length BA.

6. On a separate sheet of paper, draw a larger version of the design. Start with a golden rectangle with a long side of 10 inches.

The short side should be about $6\frac{3}{16}$ inches.

Lesson 14-4

NAME _____ DATE _____ PERIOD _____

14-4 Reading to Learn Mathematics

Probability Distributions

Pre-Activity **How can a pet store owner use a probability distribution?**

Read the introduction to Lesson 14-4 at the top of page 777 in your textbook.

- How many customers did the store owner survey? **100 customers**
- Based on the survey, it is most likely that a customer would have ____1____ pet(s) and least likely that they would have ____0____ pet(s).

Reading the Lesson

The table below shows the probability of various family sizes in the United States.

Family Size (United States)	
X = Size of Family	Probability
2	0.42
3	0.23
4	0.21
5	0.10
6	0.03
7	0.01

Source: *Statistical Abstract of the United States*

1. For each value of X, is the probability greater than or equal to 0 and less than or equal to 1? **yes**

2. What is the sum of the probabilities? **1**

3. Is the probability distribution valid? **yes**

4. Complete the probability histogram of the data.

Title: Family Size (United States)

P(X) axis: 0.60, 0.50, 0.40, 0.30, 0.20, 0.10, 0

x = Size of Family: 2, 3, 4, 5, 6, 7

Helping You Remember

5. Use the outcomes of tossing a coin to describe how the probabilities of the possible outcomes add up to 1. $P(\text{heads}) = 0.5$; $P(\text{tails}) = 0.5$; $0.5 + 0.5 = 1$

Answers (Lesson 14-5)

14-5 Study Guide and Intervention
Probability Simulations

Theoretical and Experimental Probability The probability used to describe events mathematically is called **theoretical probability**. For example, the mathematical probability of rolling a 4 with a number cube is $\frac{1}{6}$, or $P(4) = \frac{1}{6}$. **Experimental probability** is the ratio of the number of times an outcome occurs in an experiment to the total number of events or trials, known as the **relative frequency**.

Experimental probability	$\dfrac{\text{frequency of an outcome}}{\text{total number of trials}}$

Example 1 **Matt recorded that it rained 8 times in November and snowed 3 times. The other days, it was sunny. There are 30 days in November. Suppose Matt uses these results to predict November's weather next year. What is the probability that a day in November will be sunny?**

$$
\begin{aligned}
\text{Experimental Probability} &= \frac{\text{frequency of outcome}}{\text{total number of trials}} \\
&= \frac{(30 - 8 - 3)}{30} \\
&= \frac{19}{30} = 63.3\%
\end{aligned}
$$

The probability that it will be sunny on a day in November is 63.3%.

Example 2 **A football team noticed that 9 of the last 20 coin tosses to choose which team would receive the ball first resulted in tails. What is the experimental probability of the coin landing on tails? What is the theoretical probability?**

$$
\begin{aligned}
\text{Experimental Probability} &= \frac{\text{frequency of outcome}}{\text{total number of trials}} \\
&= \frac{\text{number of tails}}{\text{total number of tosses}} \\
&= \frac{9}{20} = 45\%
\end{aligned}
$$

In this case, the experimental probability that a coin toss will be tails is 45%. If the coin is fair, the mathematical probability is 50%.

Exercises

A math class decided to test whether a die is fair, that is, whether the experimental probability equals the theoretical probability. The results for 100 rolls are shown at the right. Use the information for Exercises 1–3.

1: 1	2: 15
3: 4	4: 13
5: 15	6: 42

1. What is the theoretical probability of rolling a 6? **16.7%**

2. What is the experimental probability of rolling a 6? **42%**

3. Is the die fair? Explain your reasoning.
Probably not; theoretical probability ≠ experimental probability.

14-5 Study Guide and Intervention (continued)
Probability Simulations

Performing Simulations A method that is often used to find experimental probability is a **simulation**. A simulation allows you to use objects to act out an event that would be difficult or impractical to perform.

Example **In one baseball season, Pete was able to get a base hit 42 times he was at bat.**

a. What could be used to simulate his getting a base hit?

First find the experimental probability.

$$
\begin{aligned}
\text{Experimental Probability} &= \frac{\text{frequency of outcome}}{\text{total number of trials}} \\
&= \frac{42}{254} \text{ or } 16.5\%
\end{aligned}
$$

Notice that the experimental probability is about $\frac{1}{6}$. Therefore use a spinner like the one at the right with 6 equally likely outcomes.

b. Describe a way to simulate his next 10 times at bat.

Let an outcome of 1 correspond to Pete's getting a base hit. Let all other outcomes correspond to his *not* getting a hit. Spin the spinner once to simulate a time at bat. Record the result and repeat this 9 more times.

Exercises

1. What could you use to simulate the outcome of guessing on a 20 question true-false test?
Sample answer: a coin tossed 20 times with heads corresponding to true and tails corresponding to false

2. What could you use to simulate the outcome of guessing on a 20-question multiple choice test with 4 alternative answers labeled A, B, C, and D for each question?
Sample answer: a spinner with 4 equal-sized sections labeled A, B, C, and D spun 20 times

For Exercises 3–4, use the following information.
Main Street Supermarket randomly gives each shopper a free two-liter bottle of cola during the Saturday shopping hours. The supermarket sells 6 different types of cola.

3. What could be used to perform a simulation of this situation? **Sample answer: a spinner with 6 equal-sized sections labeled to represent the 6 types of cola**

4. How could you use this simulation to model the next 50 bottles of cola given out.
Sample answer: spin the spinner described for Exercise 3 fifty times

5. At a picnic, there were 2 peanut butter sandwiches, 2 chicken sandwiches, a tuna sandwich, and a turkey sandwich in a cooler. Describe a simulation that could be used to find the probability of randomly picking a certain sandwich from the cooler.
Sample answer: If rolling a number cube results in a 1 or 2, choose peanut butter; 3 or 4, choose chicken; 5, choose tuna; 6, choose turkey

NAME _____ DATE _____ PERIOD _____

14-5 Skills Practice
Probability Simulations

For Exercises 1–3, use a standard deck of 52 cards. Select a card at random, record the suit of the card (heart, diamond, club, or spade), and then replace the card. Repeat this procedure 26 times.

1. Based on your results, what is the experimental probability of selecting a heart? **Answers will vary. The theoretical probability is 0.25.**

2. Based on your results, what is the experimental probability of selecting a diamond or a spade? **Answers will vary. The theoretical probability is 0.5.**

3. Compare your results to the theoretical probabilities. **The theoretical probability in Exercise 1 is 0.25 and in Exercise 2 is 0.5.**

4. There are 3 siblings in the Bencievenga family. What could you use to simulate the genders of the 3 siblings? **Sample answer: three coins, one for each of the siblings, with tails for male and heads for female, or 1 coin tossed three times**

5. A random survey of 23 students revealed that 2 students walk to school, 12 ride the bus, 6 drive a car, and 3 ride with a parent or other adult. What could you use for a simulation to determine the probability that a student selected at random uses any one type of transportation? **Sample answer: Use differently-colored marbles that match in number with the survey for each transportation type.**

BIOLOGY For Exercises 6–9, use the following information.

Stephen conducted a survey of the students in his classes to observe the distribution of eye color. The table shows the results of his survey.

Eye Color	Blue	Brown	Green	Hazel
Number	12	58	2	8

6. Find the experimental probability distribution for each eye color.
$P(Blue) = 0.15$, $P(Brown) = 0.725$, $P(Green) = 0.025$, $P(Hazel) = 0.1$

7. Based on the survey, what is the experimental probability that a student in Stephen's classes has blue or green eyes? **0.175**

8. Based on the survey, what is the experimental probability that a student in Stephen's classes does *not* have green or hazel eyes? **0.875**

9. If the distribution of eye color in Stephen's grade is similar to the distribution in his classes, about how many of the 360 students in his grade would be expected to have brown eyes? **about 261**

NAME _____ DATE _____ PERIOD _____

14-5 Practice (Average)
Probability Simulations

For Exercises 1–3, place 5 red, 4 yellow, and 7 green marbles in a box. Randomly draw two marbles from the box, record each color, and then return the marbles to the box. Repeat this procedure 50 times.

1. Based on your results, what is the experimental probability of selecting two yellow marbles? **Answers will vary. The theoretical probability is 0.05.**

2. Based on your results, what is the experimental probability of selecting a green marble and a yellow marble? **Answers will vary. The theoretical probability is about 0.233.**

3. Compare your results to the theoretical probabilities. **The theoretical probability in Exercise 1 is 0.05, and in Exercise 2 is about 0.233.**

4. Color blindness occurs in 4% of the male population. What could you use to simulate this situation? **Sample answer: a deck of playing cards in which 1 card is red and 24 are black**

SCHOOL CURRICULUM For Exercises 5–8, use the following information.

Laurel Woods High randomly selected students for a survey to determine the most important school issues among the student body. The school wants to develop a curriculum that addresses these issues. The survey results are shown in the table.

School Issues	
Issue	Number Ranking Issue Most Important
Grades	37
School Standards	17
Popularity	84
Dating	76
Violence	68
Drugs, including tobacco	29

5. Find the experimental probability distribution of the importance of each issue.
$P(Grades) \approx 0.119$, $P(School Standards) \approx 0.055$, $P(Popularity) \approx 0.270$, $P(Dating) \approx 0.244$, $P(Violence) \approx 0.219$, $P(Drugs) \approx 0.093$

6. Based on the survey, what is the experimental probability that a student chosen at random thinks the most important issue is grades or school standards? **about 0.174**

7. The enrollment in the 9th and 10th grades at Laurel Woods High is 168. If their opinions are reflective of those of the school as a whole, how many of them would you expect to have popularity as the most important issue? **about 45**

8. Suppose the school develops a curriculum incorporating the top three issues. What is the probability that a student selected at random will think the curriculum addresses the most important issue at school? **about 0.733**

Lesson 14-5

Answers

NAME _____ DATE _____ PERIOD _____

14-5 Reading to Learn Mathematics
Probability Simulations

Pre-Activity How can probability simulations be used in health care?

Read the introduction to Lesson 14-5 at the top of page 782 in your textbook.

- What does success mean in this study? **condition improved**

- Since there were 100 people in each study group, what does each number in the chart represent? **percent of people in the study group**

Reading the Lesson

For each situation described below, choose the manipulative you would use to simulate the problem. Explain your choice.

	Situation	Simulation method
1.	58% of drivers (commercial and private vehicles) have a cell phone in their car. Simulate whether or not the next 10 drivers you meet on the road will have a cell phone.	• die • coins • marbles • spinner **Sample answer: spinner; The spinner could be in two parts, one using 58% of the space, the other using 42%. The spinner landing in the 58% region would indicate a cell-phone user.**
2.	A restaurant has six types of coloring books to give away with children's meals. Simulate finding which coloring books are given away with the next 15 children's meals that are ordered.	• die • coins • marbles • spinner **Sample answer: number cube; Let each number represent one type of coloring book. Roll the cube 15 times, and record the numbers that are rolled.**

Helping You Remember

3. In your own words, explain the difference between theoretical probability and experimental probability.

Theoretical probability describes what should happen, and experimental probability describes what has been observed.

NAME _____ DATE _____ PERIOD _____

14-5 Enrichment

The Work Problem and Similar Right Triangles

"The work problem" has been included in algebra textbooks for a very long time. In older books, the people in the problem always seemed to be digging ditches.

If Olivia can dig a ditch in x hours and George can dig the same ditch in y hours, how long will it take them to dig the ditch if they work together?

You have learned a way to solve this type of problem using rational equations. It can also be solved using a geometric model that uses two overlapping right triangles.

In the drawing, the length x is Olivia's time. The length y is George's time. The answer to the problem is the length of the segment z. The distance $m + n$ can be any convenient length.

Solve each problem.

1. Solve the work problem for $x = 6$ and $y = 3$ by drawing a diagram and measuring.

   1 h = 0.5 cm z = 2 hours

   Students' scales will vary.

2. Confirm your solution to Exercise 1 by writing and solving a rational equation.

   $\frac{t}{6} + \frac{t}{3} = 1$ or $\frac{1}{6} + \frac{1}{3} = \frac{1}{t}$; $t = 2$

3. On a separate sheet of paper, create a word problem to go with the values $x = 6$ and $y = 3$. **Answers will vary.**

4. On a separate sheet of paper, solve this problem with a diagram. Use centimeters and measure to the nearest tenth. Olivia can wash a car in 3 hours. George can wash a car in 4 hours. How long will it take them working together to wash one car? **about 1.7 hours**

5. Triangles that have the same shape are called *similar triangles*. You may have learned that corresponding sides of similar triangles form equal ratios. Using the drawing at the top of the page, you can thus conclude that Equations A and B below are true. Use the equations to prove the formula for the work problem.

Equation A	Equation B	Work Formula
$\frac{z}{x} = \frac{n}{m+n}$	$\frac{z}{y} = \frac{m}{m+n}$	$\frac{1}{x} + \frac{1}{y} = \frac{1}{z}$

Adding equations A and B gives $\frac{z}{x} + \frac{z}{y} = \frac{m+n}{m+n}$. So, $\frac{z}{x} + \frac{z}{y} = 1$.

Dividing both sides by z gives $\frac{1}{x} + \frac{1}{y} = \frac{1}{z}$.

Lesson 14-5

Chapter 14 Assessment Answer Key

Form 1
Page 861

1. __A__

2. __B__

3. __D__

4. __C__

5. __A__

6. __B__

7. __C__

8. __D__

9. __A__

10. __A__

11. __B__

Page 862

12. __D__

13. __C__

14. __B__

15. __D__

16. __B__

17. __C__

18. __D__

19. __A__

20. __B__

B: __RR, RY, RB, YR, YY,__ __YB, BR, BY, BB; $\frac{1}{3}$__

Form 2A
Page 863

1. __C__

2. __B__

3. __D__

4. __B__

5. __A__

6. __C__

7. __A__

8. __D__

9. __C__

10. __B__

11. __D__

12. __A__

(continued on the next page)

Chapter 14 Assessment Answer Key

Form 2A *(continued)*
Page 864

13. __D__

14. __B__

15. __B__

16. __A__

17. __A__

18. __C__

19. __A__

20. __B__

B: _____ $n = 8$ _____

Form 2B
Page 865

1. __B__

2. __D__

3. __A__

4. __A__

5. __B__

6. __D__

7. __C__

8. __A__

9. __C__

10. __B__

11. __A__

12. __D__

Page 866

13. __B__

14. __A__

15. __D__

16. __A__

17. __A__

18. __B__

19. __B__

20. __C__

B: _____ $n = 5$ or $n = 1$ _____

Chapter 14 Assessment Answer Key

Form 2C

1. HH, HT, TH, TT

2. DS, DU, NS, NU OS, OU

3. 60

4. 105

5. 1001

6. 2730

7. 924

8. 5040

9. $\dfrac{91}{820}$

10. $\dfrac{27}{41}$

11. $\dfrac{1}{6}$

12. $\dfrac{4}{13}$

13. $\dfrac{45}{112}$

14. $\dfrac{17}{56}$

15. 0.264 + 0.087 + 0.223 + 0.162 + 0.203 + 0.061 = 1

16. 0.426

17. $\dfrac{16}{25}$

18. 77

19. Sample answer: a 6-sided die with each of the first 3 booths being represented by a side and the 4th booth being represented by 3 sides

20. $\dfrac{1}{5}$

B: 6048

Chapter 14 Assessment Answer Key

Form 2D

Page 869

1. RH, RT, BH, BT

2. LB, LG, LW, TB
   TG, TW

3. 72

4. 120

5. 220

6. 524,160

7. 3003

8. 6720

9. $\dfrac{105}{703}$

10. $\dfrac{23}{38}$

11. $\dfrac{2}{9}$

12. $\dfrac{4}{13}$

13. $\dfrac{21}{58}$

14. $\dfrac{9}{29}$

Page 870

15. 0.027 + 0.213 +
    0.384 + 0.203+
    0.123 + 0.050 = 1

16. 0.173

17. $\dfrac{31}{50}$

18. 868

19. Sample answer:
    a 6-sided die with
    the first company
    being represented
    by 4 sides and
    each of the other
    2 companies being
    represented by
    a side

20. $\dfrac{2}{15}$

B: 1260

Chapter 14 Assessment Answer Key

Form 3
Page 871

1. VAS, VAP, VAD,
   VWS, VWP, VWD,
   BAS, BAP, BAD,
   BWS, BWP, BWD

2. HG, HR, HB, HO
   TG, TR, TB, TO

3. 362,880

4. 480

5. $\frac{66}{13}$

6. 1440

7. 3,991,680

8. $\frac{189}{1615}$

9. $\frac{224}{1035}$

10. $\frac{272}{1035}$

11. $\frac{17}{26}$

12. $\frac{34}{53}$

Page 872

13. $P(X = 1) = \frac{1}{6}$; $P(X = 2) = \frac{5}{36}$
    $P(X = 3) = \frac{25}{216}$

14. $\frac{125}{216}$

15. 28

16. 0.803

17. $\frac{124}{165}$

18. 65

19. Sample answer: a bag with 12 differently colored marbles and a spinner divided in 3 equal parts

20. $\frac{39}{80}$

B: $\frac{38}{462}$ or about 8%

Chapter 14 Assessment Answer Key

Page 873, Open-Ended Assessment
Scoring Rubric

Score	General Description	Specific Criteria
4	**Superior** A correct solution that is supported by well-developed, accurate explanations	• Shows thorough understanding of the concepts of *permutations, combinations, independent and dependent events, mutually exclusive and inclusive events, random variables, probability distributions,* and *experimental and theoretical probability.* • Uses appropriate strategies to solve problems. • Computations are correct. • Written explanations are exemplary. • Goes beyond requirements of some or all problems.
3	**Satisfactory** A generally correct solution, but may contain minor flaws in reasoning or computation	• Shows an understanding of the concepts of *permutations, combinations, independent and dependent events, mutually exclusive and inclusive events, random variables, probability distributions,* and *experimental and theoretical probability.* • Uses appropriate strategies to solve problems. • Computations are mostly correct. • Written explanations are effective. • Satisfies all requirements of problems.
2	**Nearly Satisfactory** A partially correct interpretation and/or solution to the problem	• Shows an understanding of most of the concepts of *permutations, combinations, independent and dependent events, mutually exclusive and inclusive events, random variables, probability distributions,* and *experimental and theoretical probability.* • May not use appropriate strategies to solve problems. • Computations are mostly correct. • Written explanations are satisfactory. • Satisfies the requirements of most of the problems.
1	**Nearly Unsatisfactory** A correct solution with no supporting evidence or explanation	• Final computation is correct. • No written explanations or work is shown to substantiate the final computation. • Satisfies minimal requirements of some of the problems.
0	**Unsatisfactory** An incorrect solution indicating no mathematical understanding of the concept or task, or no solution is given	• Shows little or no understanding of most of the concepts of *permutations, combinations, independent and dependent events, mutually exclusive and inclusive events, random variables, probability distributions,* and *experimental and theoretical probability.* • Does not use appropriate strategies to solve problems. • Computations are incorrect. • Written explanations are unsatisfactory. • Does not satisfy requirements of problems. • No answer may be given.

Chapter 14 Assessment Answer Key

Page 873, Open-Ended Assessment
Sample Answers

In addition to the scoring rubric found on page A22, the following sample answers may be used as guidance in evaluating open-ended assessment items.

1a. The use of the word *combination* in this phrase does not match the mathematical definition. Since the dial must be turned to numbers in a specific order, the student should conclude that from the mathematical definitions this type of lock could be referred to as a *permutation* lock.

1b. The use of the word *combination* in this phrase does match the mathematical definition. In this phrase the word *combination* is referring to a specific grouping of items from the menu, but the student should recognize that the order of the items is not important.

1c. The use of the word *combination* in this phrase does not match the mathematical definition. Since the pool balls hit each other in a specified order, the student should conclude that from the mathematical definitions this type of shot could be referred to as a *permutation* shot.

1d. The use of the word *combination* in this phrase does match the mathematical definition. In this phrase the word *combination* is referring to a grouping, but the student should recognize that the order is not important.

2a. Sample answer: How many computers do you own? Do you own a scanner?; The events of owning 2 computers and owning a scanner are independent events.; The events of owning 3 computers and not owning a scanner are inclusive events.

2b. Sample answer: How many hours per day do you use a computer?

X = Number of Hours	Number of People
0	8
1	11
2	14
3 or more	17

X = Number of Hours	Probability
0	0.16
1	0.22
2	0.28
3 or more	0.34

3a. The student should recognize this as a theoretical probability.

3b. Since the probability is equal to the ratio of the frequency of the event to the size of the sample space, the student should recognize this as an experimental probability.

4a. The student should describe an event that has exactly 2 equally likely outcomes.

4b. The student should describe an event that consists of 2 separate events combined or 1 event with 2 distinct parts. In either case both events or parts should have exactly 2 equally likely outcomes each.

5. Sample answer:
$$_nP_r = (r!)(_nC_r); n = 7, r = 3$$
$$_7P_3 = \frac{7!}{(7-3)!} = \frac{3! \cdot 7!}{3!(7-3)!} = 3!\frac{7!}{3!(7-3)!}$$
$$= (3!)(_7C_3)$$

Chapter 14 Assessment Answer Key

1. event

2. factorial

3. Fundamental Counting Principle

4. tree diagram

5. sample space

6. complements

7. random variable

8. probability histogram

9. Relative frequency

10. empirical study

11. A probability distribution is the probability of every possible value of a random variable *X*.

12. A compound event is an event made up of two or more simple events.

Quiz (Lessons 14–1 and 14–2)
Page 875

1. CF, CB, CS, VF, VB, VS

2. HHH, HHT, HTH, HTT, THH, THT, TTH, TTT

3. 120

4. 479,001,600

5. 40

6. permutation; order is important

7. combination; order is not important

8. 5040

9. 28

10. D

Quiz (Lesson 14–3)
Page 875

1. $\dfrac{15}{64}$

2. $\dfrac{3}{28}$

3. $\dfrac{2}{13}$

4. $\dfrac{4}{13}$

5. $\dfrac{17}{26}$

Quiz (Lesson 14–4)
Page 876

	1	2	3	4	5	6
1	0	1	2	3	4	5
2	1	0	1	2	3	4
3	2	1	0	1	2	3
4	3	2	1	0	1	2
5	4	3	2	1	0	1
6	5	4	3	2	1	0

1.

2. $P(X=2)=\dfrac{2}{9}$, $P(X=3)=\dfrac{1}{6}$
$P(X=4)=\dfrac{1}{9}$

3. $\dfrac{4}{9}$

4. 0.41

5. 39 households

Quiz (Lesson 14–5)
Page 876

1. $P(\text{1 Family Member})=\dfrac{7}{52}$
$P(\text{2 Family Members})=\dfrac{5}{26}$
$P(\text{3 Family Members})=\dfrac{43}{130}$

2. $\dfrac{35}{52}$

3. Sample answer: roll a die

4. Sample answer: use a spinner divided into 4 parts

5. Sample answer: toss 3 coins

Chapter 14 Assessment Answer Key

Mid-Chapter Test
Page 877

1. __D__

2. __A__

3. __B__

4. __B__

5. __A__

6. __900__

7. __15,120__

8. __1001__

9. __$\dfrac{12}{175}$__

10. __$\dfrac{47}{100}$__

11. __8__

1st Child	2nd Child	3rd Child	Outcomes
B	B	B	BBB
		G	BBG
	G	B	BGB
		G	BGG
G	B	B	GBB
		G	GBG
	G	B	GGB
		G	GGG

Cumulative Review
Page 878

1. __$\dfrac{1}{2}$, 1, 2__

2. __(−2, −2)__

3. __$4a^2 - 12ab^2 + 9b^4$__

4. __$6abc^2$__

5. __3__

6. __$(m + 1)(m + 3)$__

7. __$\dfrac{x^2 - 4x - 4}{x^2 - 2x + 4}$__

8. __2-by-3; second row, third column__

9. __3–5 pets__

10. __There is a gap in the 7–9 pets measurement class. The data appear to be skewed to the left.__

11. __16__

12. __161; 700__

13. __$\dfrac{4}{13}$__

Chapter 14 Assessment Answer Key

Standardized Test Practice

Page 879

1. Ⓐ ⬤B Ⓒ Ⓓ

2. Ⓔ Ⓕ Ⓖ ⬤H

3. ⬤A Ⓑ Ⓒ Ⓓ

4. Ⓔ Ⓕ ⬤G Ⓗ

5. Ⓐ Ⓑ Ⓒ ⬤D

6. ⬤E Ⓕ Ⓖ Ⓗ

7. Ⓐ Ⓑ ⬤C Ⓓ

8. Ⓔ Ⓕ ⬤G Ⓗ

9. Ⓐ ⬤B Ⓒ Ⓓ

Page 880

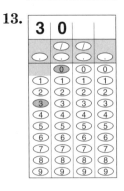

10. **2 | 7** — 27

11. **2 | 4** — 24

12. **3** — 3

13. **3 | 0** — 30

14. Ⓐ Ⓑ Ⓒ ⬤D

15. ⬤A Ⓑ Ⓒ Ⓓ

16. Ⓐ ⬤B Ⓒ Ⓓ

17. Ⓐ ⬤B Ⓒ Ⓓ

Chapter 14 Assessment Answer Key

Unit 5 Test

Page 881

1. a group of articles of clothing; all articles of clothing made by the manufacturer; unbiased; systematic

2. 40 shoppers; all people who can exercise; biased; convenience

3. 3-by-4; third row, second column

4. $\begin{bmatrix} 6 & 11 & 6 \\ 20 & 6 & -2 \end{bmatrix}$

5. 10–20 dollars per hour

6.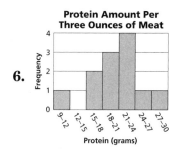

Protein Amount Per Three Ounces of Meat

7. 20.5; 17.5; 23

8. 16; 5.5; none

9.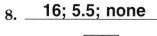

10. set A

Page 882

11. 120

12.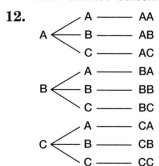

Math Science Outcomes

```
        A ——— AA
A <     B ——— AB
        C ——— AC

        A ——— BA
B <     B ——— BB
        C ——— BC

        A ——— CA
C <     B ——— CB
        C ——— CC
```

13. 479,001,600

14. 4845

15. $\dfrac{4}{663}$

16. $\dfrac{7}{13}$

17. 0.02 + 0.40 + 0.06 + 0.40 + 0.12 = 1

18. 0.58

19. $\dfrac{15}{50}$ or 30%

20. $\dfrac{9}{50}$ or 18%

Answers

Chapter 14 Assessment Answer Key

Second Semester Test

Page 883

1. __C__

2. __B__

3. __C__

4. __C__

5. __A__

6. __D__

7. __B__

8. __A__

9. __D__

10. __B__

11. __D__

Page 884

12. __A__

13. __B__

14. __A__

15. __D__

16. __B__

17. __A__

18. __D__

19. __C__

20. __C__

(continued on the next page)

Chapter 14 Assessment Answer Key

Second Semester Test (continued)

Page 885

21. elimination (+); (1, 2)

22. substitution; (−3, 4)

23. elimination (×); (−1, 2)

24.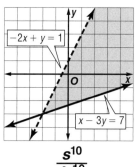

25. $\dfrac{s^{10}}{4r^{10}}$

26. 4.56×10^{-1}; 0.456

27. $6x^2 - 5x - 5$

28. $x^2 + 2x$

29. $2y^2 - y - 21$

30. $(t - 1)(t - 6)$

31. $3(x + 2)(x - 2)(x + 1)$

32. $\left\{ \dfrac{2}{7}, 5 \right\}$

33. $\{-1, 4\}$

34. $\{-1.5, 0.9\}$

35. 1; 15

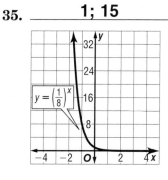

Page 886

36. 768

37. 4

38. No; $9^2 + 24^2 \neq 26^2$

39. 5, 35

40. $\dfrac{60}{7}$

41. $m\angle A = 17°$, $AC = 25.8$, $BC = 7.9$

42. $\dfrac{m - 4}{m - 1}$

43. $2x + 9 + \dfrac{22}{x - 3}$

44. $\dfrac{11y + 16}{4(y + 1)}$

45. $\dfrac{(z + 1)(z - 1)}{(z + 2)(z - 2)}$

46. $-\dfrac{3}{4}$

47. 13; 37; 33; 39; 6; none

48. $\dfrac{2}{7}$

Answers

Chapter 14 Assessment Answer Key

Final Test

1. __B__

2. __C__

3. __A__

4. __A__

5. __D__

6. __C__

7. __B__

8. __D__

9. __D__

10. __B__

11. __A__

12. __C__

13. __A__

14. __B__

15. __D__

16. __A__

17. __C__

18. __D__

19. __C__

20. __C__

21. __B__

Chapter 14 Assessment Answer Key

Page 889

22. __A__

23. __C__

24. __A__

25. __A__

26. __B__

27. __A__

28. __D__

29. __B__

30. __B__

31. __C__

Page 890

32. __$20m + 18n$__

33. __H: I go to Hawaii;__
    C: I am on vacation;
    If I go to Hawaii then I
    am on vacation.

34. __2__

35. __1:4__

36. __irrational numbers__

37. __$15 - t = \left(7 + \dfrac{t}{2}\right) + 4$__

38. __0__

39. __$88.40__

40. __2 lb__

41. __$Q'(1, 1)$, $R'(3, 1)$,__
    $S'(4, 3)$, $T'(2, 3)$;

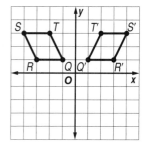

42. __{(−3, −1), (−2, 1), (−1, −2),__
    (0, 1), (1, 0), (2, −1)};
    {(−1, −3), (1, −2), (−2, −1),
    (1, 0), (0, 1), (−1, 2)}

43. __−2; −4__

44. __0__

Glencoe Algebra 1

Chapter 14 Assessment Answer Key

Final Test *(continued)*

45. $y = 9x - 28$

46. $y = -\dfrac{3}{4}x + 6$

47. $\{b \mid b > -3\}$

48. $\{m \mid m < -2 \text{ or } m > 3\}$

49. $\{h \mid 65.5 \le h \le 70.5\}$

50.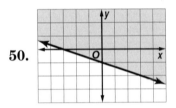

51. $(-1, 2)$

52. $(-7, 9)$

53. $52°$ and $38°$

54.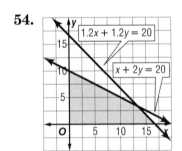

55. $-\dfrac{8m^6}{n^{12}}$

56. $\dfrac{2}{5}$

57. $3x^3 + x^2 + 10x - 8$

58. $(2m - 7n)^2$

59. $2(x + 3)(x - 3)(x + 2)$

60. $\left\{\dfrac{2}{7}, 4\right\}$

61. $\{-4, 0, 4\}$

62. $x = -1; (-1, -3)$

63. $\{-4.9, 0.9\}$

64. Yes; the domain values are at regular intervals and the range values have a common factor 2.

65. 896

66. $\dfrac{\sqrt{5a}}{3b}$

67. 24

68. 6 ft

69. 208 ft

70. $xy = -64; -40$

71. $\dfrac{m - 1}{m - 2}; -1, 2$

72. $x^2 + 3x - 4$

73. $\begin{bmatrix} -44 & 8 & 2 \\ 5 & -47 & 61 \end{bmatrix}$